Welcome to our very first Puffin Annual! We hope that from the moment when you start tracing your way through Jill McDonald's marvellous maze until the time (how many weeks later?) when you work out which Puffin has caught the biggest fish, you will find in it all the things that please you most.

Planning an Annual is rather like cooking a delicious meal. We had to collect as many interesting, imaginative and unusual ingredients as possible from as many distinguished Puffin authors and artists as we could persuade to join us. Then we added a handful of experts and some celebrities, a few sentimental memories of the early Puffin Posts, and eureka here it is! Making it has given us a lot of pleasure and we hope most of it spills over to you. **K.W.**

Contributors we are proud to have in this issue

STORIES BY—

Joan Aiken, Roald Dahl, Nicholas Fisk, Russell Hoban, Norman Hunter, Tove Jansson, Barbara Sleigh

ARTICLES, FEATURES AND POEMS BY—

Edward Ardizzone, Conrad Bailey, Nina Bawden, Elisabeth Beresford, Quentin Blake, Michael Bond, Bruce Carter, Peter Dickinson, Leon Garfield, Charles Gibbs-Smith, Michael Grater, Griselda Greaves, Roger Lancelyn Green, Joyce Grenfell, Cynthia Harnett, Brenda Johnson, Yehudi Menuhin, Jill Paton Walsh, John Ryan, Sheila Sancha, Geoffrey Trease, HRH The Prince of Wales.

PUZZLES, RIDDLES AND CARTOONS BY—

Mel Calman, Remy Charlip, Gunvor Edwards, Michael Holt, Jill McDonald

PAINTINGS AND DRAWINGS BY—

George Adamson, Scoular Anderson, Pauline Baynes, Raymond Briggs, Anthony Colbert, Peter Edwards, Hans Helweg, John Vernon Lord, Anthony Maitland, Graham Round, Krystyna Turska, Fritz Wegner

Cover and end papers by Jill McDonald

EDITED BY—

Treld Bicknell, Frank Waters, Kaye Webb

The editors would like to thank the following for their kind permission to reproduce photographs appearing in this Annual. A. F. Kersting, pp. 23-26; Picturepoint, p. 23; L. Hugh Newman and Frank Lane, Eric Hoskings, pp. 39-42; Aerofilms Ltd, p. 47; John Ryan, pp. 65, 66; Nelson Hargreaves, p. 71; Roger Hill and John Phillips, pp. 79-82, 95, 116; John Hunnex, pp. 120-3; Mary Evans Picture Library, pp. 120, 121; Chris Smith of the *Observer*, pp. 124, 125; Mervyn Rees, p. 125; Sport & General Press Agency Ltd, pp. 124, 125.

Puffin Books: a Division of Penguin Books Ltd, Harmondsworth, Middlesex, England.
Penguin Books Inc., 7110 Ambassador Road, Baltimore, Maryland 21207, U.S.A.
Penguin Books Australia Ltd, Ringwood, Victoria, Australia
Penguin Books Canada Ltd, 41 Steelcase Road West, Markham, Ontario, Canada
Penguin Books (N.Z.) Ltd, 182-190 Wairau Road, Auckland 10, New Zealand
This Annual first published by Puffin Books, 1974.
Copyright © Penguin Books Ltd., 1974.
Made and printed in Great Britain by Purnell & Sons Ltd, Paulton (Somerset) and London

This anthology copyright © Penguin Books Ltd, 1974
THE FAITHLESS LOLLYBIRD, © 1974 by Joan Aiken; IMPOSSIBLE PETS, © 1974 by Peter Dickinson; COLLECTING CASTLES, © 1974 by Sheila Sancha; FOUR TIMELESS TALES, © 1974 by Russell Hoban; HOW BIRDS FLY, © 1974 by Charles Gibbs-Smith; WALTER AND HIS MAGIC, © 1974 by Mel Calman; THE BOY, THE DOG AND THE SPACE SHIP, © 1974 by Nicholas Fisk; PROFESSOR BRANESTAWM GOES CUCKOO, © 1974 by Norman Hunter; LOUIS LOPPA, © by Gunvor Edwards; HERE BE DRAGONS, © 1974 by Bruce Carter; AMAZING ACHIEVEMENTS OF DAYS GONE BY, © 1974 by Quentin Blake; THE CAT, © 1974 by Tove Jansson; THE STRANGE AFFAIR OF THE WATTLE-U-EAT, © 1974 by Brenda Johnson; THAT AWFUL BOY, © 1974 by Geoffrey Trease; THE UPSIDEDOWN MICE, © 1974 by Roald Dahl; MY MOTHER'S FRILLY PARASOL, © 1974 by Cynthia Harnett

The Faithless

Story By Joan Aiken

FAR away to the north, in a small hut in the middle of a large forest, there lived a weaver whose name was Luke. All this happened not long ago as the clock ticks, but a long way off as the crow flies.

In his hut, Luke had a loom, taking up most of the floor-space. And every day, on his loom, he wove the most beautiful cloth—cloth for coats and cloaks and carpets, for sheets and shirts and shawls, for towels and tablecloths and tapestries, for babies' blankets and bishops' aprons. Some of the things he made were so beautiful that it seemed wrong to do anything but hang them on the wall and gaze at them. But everything he made was really meant to be used.

To help him with his weaving Luke had a bird, a Lollybird. When he had strung up his loom ready to start, with the woollen or cotton or silk threads going longways—the warp—Luke would tie another length of wool to a shuttle and hand it to the Lollybird, which up to that moment would have been sitting very still, either on the chimneypiece, or a corner of the loom, or Luke's shoulder, carefully watching all that he did.

However as soon as Luke handed the shuttle to it, the Lollybird would begin to fly. It flew with the most amazing speed back and forth, in and out, up and down, among the strings on the loom, going so fast that nothing of it could be seen at all except a blur of colour as it shot to and fro.

The Lollybird itself was just a little grey creature, but as it worked it would snatch one thread and then another from Luke. Sometimes, dropping the shuttle entirely, it would wind a scarlet strand round its neck and a green one round its stomach, carry a pink thread in its beak and clutch a silver one in its claws, so that if it had ever stopped, you would have thought it was a travelling Christmas tree, all sparkling and rainbow-coloured. But it never did stop until the work was finished, the last knot made and the last thread pulled tightly into place. Then with a final swoop and a last flash of its wings it would come to rest on Luke's shoulder, or the top of his head, and together they would take a careful look at the cloth they had just woven.

Perhaps it was a coronation robe for a king, all scarlet and gold, with fur round the border and a roaring lion in the middle. Or perhaps it was a carpet for a cathedral with angels and lilies and harps, all in blue and green and silver. Or it might be a tablecloth for a children's school, with cats and dogs, and the sun and moon, and birds and fish, and letters and numbers, to give the children something to look at as they were eating their dinner.

Whatever the piece of cloth was that they had just woven, Luke and his Lollybird would carefully inspect it, making sure there were no rough edges, or lumpy places, or loose threads. But there never were.

Then Luke would give a sigh of satisfaction, and say,

'Well, I think we did a good bit of

Lollybird

Illustrations by Krystyna Turska

work that time, my dear Lollybird,' and the Lollybird would cock its head on one side in approval and say,

'Certainly can't see anything wrong with that little job, master,' and the two friends would stop work for a short time.

Sometimes, in these spells off between jobs, Luke might play on his flute, while the Lollybird chirped a little song. The Lollybird had no voice to speak of, and its song sounded like somebody scratching a twig down the side of a nutmeg grater. Indeed, the Lollybird was a little embarrassed about its lack of singing ability, but Luke didn't mind. He had a mandolin as well as the flute and sometimes the Lollybird, hopping to and fro on the mandolin's strings, would scratch them with its claws and fetch out a faint thread of tune while Luke softly whistled a few matching notes. Then, if the day was a fine one, they might go for a walk in the forest, the Lollybird sitting on Luke's shoulder or flying ahead of him through the great trunks of the trees.

On these walks they searched for the leaves and flowers and roots which Luke needed to dye the silk and wool that he used in his weaving. There was a plant with golden flowers whose root gave a beautiful yellow, and a purple flower that dyed red, and a kind of toadstool which, pounded to a pulp, produced a fine dark orange, and the bark of a tree which would be ground up to make a deep rose-pink. Wild spinach gave them bright green, and certain nuts and berries were good for browns and crimsons. The only colour they could not get from any plant in the forest was a blue to satisfy them; for that, Luke had to send away many hundreds of miles. A kind of shellfish, only found in southern seas, gave a beautiful clear dark blue, but Luke often grumbled because the loads of shellfish, which had to be brought by sledge, took a long time on the way, and sometimes, if a pattern they were working on used a lot of blue, they might have to wait for a new supply to arrive.

'I wish we could find a decent blue close at hand,' Luke would say.

On their walks through the wood the two friends also found tufts of coloured moss and flower petals, bright leaves, flakes of glossy bark, gay feathers dropped by birds, even small sparkling stones and chips of rock, which they wove into their fabrics, so that often the lengths of material they made were quite dazzling and seemed to shine and ripple the way a brook does when it catches the sun's light.

Because the things he made were so beautiful, Luke's fame began to spread all over the world. More and more people wanted to buy his work. Customers came in ships and on camels, by sledge and bicycle and caravan, in lorries and balloons, on horseback and in helicopters. So that presently, after a few years had passed, Luke and his Lollybird had to work harder and harder if they were to keep up with all the orders that poured in.

'I never get a chance to sit in the sun any more,' complained the Lolly-

7

bird. 'We haven't had time for any music since the last new moon. We don't even get a breath of fresh air.'

Lately Luke had hired two boys to hunt for his dye-plants and mosses. The ones they brought back were not always so good, but there was no time for Luke and his Lollybird to go into the forest. They had to work all the hours of daylight. By the time night came the Lollybird was tired out, and would fall asleep perched on the loom with its head tucked under its wing.

'You should refuse to take any more orders,' it said to Luke one morning.

'It would be wrong to disappoint people,' said Luke. 'Specially when they have come all this way. Why, only today we had the Emperor of Japan, wanting a new dressing-gown, and the Mayor of New York, needing a carpet for his town hall, and the Queen of the Windward Islands, with an order for a screen to keep the wind off, and the President of Finland, ordering new tapestry for the Finnish—'

'Finnish? We never *shall* finish!' wailed the Lollybird, and it snatched up a shuttle and darted angrily between the warp strings of a beautiful white and silver christening shawl which they were making for a little princess in Denmark. '*She* wouldn't know the difference if they wrapped her in an old bath towel,' it muttered as it flew back and forth.

'It would be wrong to disappoint people,' repeated Luke.

'What about me? *I'm* disappointed if I don't have a bit of music, or get out for my evening stroll,' said the indignant Lollybird.

Matters became even worse. For now a railway was built through the forest, with a station right beside Luke's hut, so that more and more people could come to order things, and to watch the weavers at work. The visitors stood around, and picked up the shuttles, and tangled the wool, and were a dreadful nuisance all day

long. In the evening they invited Luke out to the cafe which had been built just down the road, and they talked to him and praised his work and asked him how he planned his patterns. He quite enjoyed all the company and cheerfulness. It made a change from the long, quiet evenings he had spent alone with the Lollybird, after it grew too dark to go on weaving, when he had nothing to do but play his flute, not very well, while the Lollybird sang its little scratchy song, like a pencil being scraped down a nutmeg grater.

The Lollybird did not enjoy all this extra company at all. It never took part in the conversation, or went out to the cafe. As soon as the light was gone it would retire to the back of the loom and go to sleep there, hidden among dangling hanks of wool, with its head under its wing. And, even during the day, when the Lollybird was working, very few people noticed it flashing to and fro under the strands of the warp, for it went faster than their eyes could follow. Many people, in fact, did not realize that the Lollybird even existed. If they praised the work and Luke said, 'Oh, it is partly the Lollybird's doing too, you know,' they believed that he was joking, and laughed politely.

So by and by he gave up mentioning the Lollybird.

One morning the Lollybird said, 'Master, it's spring. The cuckoos have come back to the forest, and the swallows are here, and the storks are building their houses, and the wild geese keep flying past, and I need to go out and stretch my wings.'

'Rubbish,' said Luke. 'You have quite enough healthy exercise flying up and down inside the loom. And we are two days late on the set of flags for the new Mandolian Republic. Hurry up and get to work.'

The Lollybird got to work, but it was sulking dreadfully as it flew backwards and forwards with the red, black, and yellow silk threads for the Mandolian flags; indeed it clutched some of the threads so tightly in its little hot angry claws that, although they did not snap immediately, the very first time that the flags were flown in a hurricane (and hurricanes are very common in Mandolia) several of them tore in half.

Now this was the first time that the Lollybird had ever done bad work. At the end of the day it felt guilty and miserable and sulkier than ever.

That evening a group of admirers called in to sit round Luke and look at the work half-finished on the loom, and praise it. They brought a bottle of wine, and presently they all began drinking and singing songs.

'Don't you keep a bird in here?' one of them asked after a while. 'Wouldn't the bird sing us a song?'

'Oh,' said Luke carelessly, 'It will be asleep by now. And in any case it's only a working-bird, not a song bird. Its song is no better than a frog croaking.'

Now the Lollybird had not been asleep. The voices and talk and laughter had kept it awake. And at these words of Luke's its heart swelled inside it with shame.

One of the visitors had left the door open a crack and, under cover of the noise and singing, which had started up again, the Lollybird crept to the end of the loom and then flew swiftly and silently out through the crack of the door, although it was black dark in the forest and none but night creatures were stirring.

The Lollybird had never been out at night. It was not accustomed to flying in the dark, and bumped into several trees. Soon it was lost. Nevertheless it flew on, listening to the songs of the nightingales and envying their voices. Presently it reached a wide open space. This was an airstrip, for now Luke had his blue shellfish flown in by plane, and there was the

freight-plane sitting in the middle of the space.

'What an enormous bird,' thought the Lollybird, for it had not had a chance to fly out that way since the plane began coming, and knew no difference.

Just then a large horned owl, which had noticed the Lollybird bumping among the trees and followed out of curiosity, swooped down to grab this clumsy stranger and missed it by no more than the flutter of a feather. The Lollybird saw two great golden eyes coming faster than a train and nipped out of the way with a skilful twist learned from years of flying up and down inside the loom.

The owl thumped against the plane's wing and the terrified Lollybird flew straight through an open hatchway and into the plane itself.

'Hooooo! Ha!' shouted the owl outside. 'I can see you, you miserable little beggar! I'm going to eat you up in one mouthful! Come out of there!'

In fact he couldn't see the Lollybird at all, and presently he gave up and flew off in search of other prey. But the Lollybird didn't know he had gone and stayed trembling in its dark

corner for a long time.

After a while the pilot arrived, climbed in, slammed the door, and started up the engine. Now the Lollybird was even more frightened, but what could it do? Nothing at all. The plane took off, circled round, climbed, higher, flew and flew through the black hours of night, until they were many many thousands of miles from the airstrip, and the forest, and Luke's little hut.

At last morning came, and the sun rose, and the plane landed, and the pilot opened the door and got down and walked away.

Then at last the Lollybird dared to come stiffly out of its hiding place and fly through the hatchway into the noise and light and muddle of a great airport.

There were so many things to see that it saw nothing at all. By pure good luck it escaped being run over by a truck, squashed flat by a crane and squeezed in a pair of automatic doors. Avoiding a Boeing 707 and a fire-wagon, and a limousine, it darted between two taxis and flew straight into the open doorway of a bus, which immediately started up and sped off along the wide straight road that led into the middle of London.

'My goodness!' thought the Lolly-bird, hanging upside down by one claw from the luggage rack and gazing out with astonishment at all the houses and supermarkets and cats and dogs and people whizzing past. 'To think there was all this in the world and I never knew it!'

In Piccadilly Circus the bus came to a stop. By this time dusk was falling and nobody noticed the Lollybird, which flew out and perched on a windowsill where it looked at the dazzling lights of the advertisements and the many-coloured cars and the people in their gay clothes and the brightly lit windows of the restaurants and the police cars and ambulances with their flashing blue beacons and the fire-engines all red and gold rushing along ringing their bells.

'My goodness,' thought the Lolly-bird again, 'I wish Luke could see this. If we had our loom here, what a picture we could weave.'

But then it remembered how angry it was with Luke. 'Anyway I can manage without him,' it thought. 'All I have to do is string a web from those prongs.'

The Lollybird began to bustle about, collecting threads and strands, of which there were plenty to be found in the untidy streets. First it drew out a long streamer of the smoke trailing from a car's exhaust pipe and wound it into a spiral, then it snatched a string from a boy's balloon, and twitched a length of raffia from a woman's shopping-basket. Here it tweaked a dangling end of wool from a girl's shawl, there it snatched a spare hair from a man's beard. All these and many other things were threaded with wonderful skill between the TV aerials that sprouted from the roofs.

Now the Lollybird really began to enjoy itself. It picked up coloured ribbons and bits of tissue paper, metal foil, orange-peel, tufts of fur from poodles, silvery rings from coke cans, and long shining strands from the tails of police horses. Everything was woven into a huge and sparkling canopy which presently dangled all over the top of Piccadilly Circus like a beautiful tent.

'Oh, what a clever Lollybird I am!' cried the Lollybird with great enthusiasm, and it flew off to do the same thing somewhere else.

Meanwhile poor Luke was in a dreadful state without his Lollybird. He had just managed to finish the job they had been working on when the Lollybird left home, but he found that he was quite unable to start

anything else. He could set up the warp, but his fingers were too clumsy for the woof. He kept dropping the shuttle, his patterns got into a muddle, and in less than two days the inside of his hut was one complete tangle of wool.

At first Luke was very angry at the Lollybird's disappearance.

He went stamping through the forest, bawling and shouting.

'Lollybird! Hey, you Lollybird! Where are you? Come back at once!'

But there was no answer.

All night he called and called. 'Where are you, you naughty Lolly-bird?'

But still there was no answer.

Then Luke began to wonder if some owl or eagle had caught the Lollybird, and to worry, and feel sorry. Then he began to remember that he had not always treated the Lollybird very well, that he had made it work when it wanted to fly out into the forest, that sometimes he had given it nothing but dry biscuits to eat for days on end, when he was too busy to stop and cook the millet porridge that the Lollybird liked best. And sometimes, he remembered, he had insisted on finishing a job of work when the Lollybird was tired and stiff, when it was yawning into its wing and having difficulty keeping its eyes open.

'Oh, my dear Lollybird! Where are you? Come back, come back, and I won't make you work so hard.'

But still there was no answer.

By this time most of the people who had come with orders for more work, or to watch and wonder at the weaving, had become impatient and gone back home again. The forest was empty and silent. But somebody, just as they left, reported that somebody else had been told that yet another person thought he had heard tell that someone else had seen the Lollybird fly off in an aeroplane.

'In that case the Lollybird may be anywhere in the world,' thought Luke. 'How shall I ever find it again? But there's no use staying here, that's certain.'

So Luke shut up his hut and climbed on to the last shellfish plane and flew to London.

When he reached London, one of the first things he heard was a story of a wonderful bird which had spread a sparkling web all over the top of Piccadilly Circus.

'Oh, that must be my Lollybird!' cried Luke, and he leapt into a taxi and told the driver to go as fast as possible to Piccadilly. Luckily Luke had plenty of money; all these years he had never spent a hundredth part of what he and the Lollybird earned between them. When he reached Piccadilly Circus he looked about for the beautiful canopy people had told him about. But the Westminster City Council Cleaning Department had come with brooms and mops and suction cleaners and had swept it down and tidied it all away.

Next Luke heard stories about a wonderful bird which had spun a cover like a huge egg-cosy, only bigger, all glittering and rainbow-coloured, over the dome of St Peter's in Rome.

'That must, that must be my wandering Lollybird!' he cried, and he took another plane and flew to Rome. But when he got to St Peter's he found that the Rome City Council had sent helicopters with hoses and had removed the wonderful cover.

'Oh,' cried Luke sorrowfully, 'where, where shall I find my wayward Lollybird?'

But now he heard tales of a marvellous bird that was weaving a multi-coloured canopy over the elephant house in the Berlin Zoo.

He sent a telegram: 'Please, please do not stop the bird,' and jumped into another plane and flew to Berlin.

When he reached the Berlin Zoo everybody was watching in admiration as the tiny bird flew darting about, snatching a hank of wool from a llama, catching a plume from the tail of an ostrich, gathering a tuft of black fur from a gorilla, whisking up a dropped peacock's feather, and a bright scale that some fish had cast off, and weaving them all into its beautiful sparkling web, while a whole ring of elephants stood underneath and gazed at it spellbound with uplifted trunks.

'Oh,' cried Luke in rapture, 'it is, it must be, my faithless Lollybird!'

And the Lollybird heard his voice among all the other voices in the crowd and answered him,

'Yes I am, I am your faithless Lollybird!'

'Come back, come back, you naughty thoughtless Lollybird! I can't manage without you!'

'No,' said the Lollybird, 'you can't manage without me, but I can manage very well without you. Goodbye, I'm off to London again.'

And it flew tauntingly away with a flip of its tail.

Poor Luke had to follow as best he could. There was no plane just then, so he caught a boat. When it came chugging up the Thames he saw that the naughty Lollybird had woven a glittering web across Tower Bridge, all made of straw winebottle-cases, and scraps of polystyrene, and bus tickets, and milk-bottle tops.

But when Luke stepped off the boat, just too late, the vagrant Lollybird flew gaily away, crying,

'You can't manage without me, but I can manage very well without you!'

'Come back! Come back to your

proper work, you wicked Lollybird!'

'Not yet! Not yet! Maybe never at all. Not till you have called me a hundred, hundred times, not till you have found a blue dye in the forest, not till I can sing as well as the nightingales, not till you promise never to overwork me ever again!'

'I promise now!' cried the sorrowful Luke.

'Promises cost nothing. You'll have to prove you are telling the truth before I believe you,' replied the uncaring Lollybird, and away it flew.

Luke didn't know what to do. He rented a room with a telephone, he rang up the police, he put advertisements in all the papers, saying, 'LOST! My faithless Lollybird. Large reward to finder.'

Many people had seen the elusive Lollybird, and rang up to say so, but wherever it had been seen, by the time Luke arrived, the bird was always gone. Luke wandered through the streets of London by day and night, calling and crying,

'Where are you, you mocking Lollybird? Where are you, you thankless Lollybird?'

Then Luke began to hear that the bird had been seen at concerts, and at schools where pupils were taught singing.

One night Luke went to a concert at the Royal Festival Hall. Sure enough, there was the Lollybird, perched on the conductor's rostrum, listening hard to the music. After a while, though, it couldn't resist beginning to flit about and pick things up here and there, a gold thread from a lady's evening cape, a white hair from the conductor's head, a fern frond out of a pot of growing plants, a tie from a flute-player's neck, a length of spaghetti from a plate in the restaurant. Then it began to weave a web across from the bows of the violinists to the boxes on the opposite side of the hall.

The violinists couldn't play with their bows tied down, the music came to a stop, and Luke cried out,

'Lollybird! You are behaving very badly. Come back to your master!'

'Not yet! Not yet! I'm having far too good a time to come home,' replied the teasing Lollybird, and away it flew, through a window and across the Thames into a great hotel where it tied all the table-napkins into a fluttering string and knotted them round the chandelier.

Luke was tired out and went back to his room to bed.

But by now the provoking Lollybird had learned how to use the telephone. Luke had no sooner gone off to sleep than the phone would ring and when he picked up the receiver he heard a shrill voice calling in his ear, 'Hullo, hullo, hullo, hullo, this is your faithless Lollybird!'

13

Night after night the Lollybird woke him in this way until Luke grew pale and thin, and had great black circles under his eyes.

'Come back! Come back you heartless Lollybird,' he cried into the telephone.

'Not yet! Not for a long time yet!'

The Lollybird was taking singing lessons from a famous opera singer. In exchange for the lessons it was weaving her a beautiful cloak from brown paper and string and bits of tinsel and pine-needles and photographers' flash-bulbs. The Lollybird wove its web, and the singer sang scales, and the Lollybird repeated them; its voice was growing louder and sweeter with every lesson. And at the end of each lesson it would borrow the singer's telephone to ring up Luke and call,

'Hullo, hullo, hullo, hullo! This is your faithless Lollybird.'

'Come back home. Come back and do your proper work!'

'Not till you have called me a hundred, hundred times,' replied the wayward bird, and it sang Luke a snatch of music from The Magic Flute, and plunked down the receiver.

Now, by chance, Luke heard tell of a famous echo, in a cave in a valley in Derbyshire, an echo that would repeat the same word for half an hour at a time, throwing it from one side of the valley to the other. So he took a train, and a bus, and a taxi, and went to the cave. The Lollybird and it flew after Luke secretly to see what he was up to, and perched on a bush outside the entrance to the cave.

'Lollybird!' cried Luke inside the tunnel. 'Come back, come back, come back to your proper work, you teasing Lollybird!'

A hundred times he called it, and each word was repeated by the echo a hundred times, so that the whole valley was filled with Luke's voice calling 'Come back, come back, come back!'

'Well, well, perhaps I will, some day,' said the Lollybird, darting about the valley, listening to all the echoes, and cocking its head on one side to count them. 'But not just yet, not just yet, my dear master!'

And away it flew.

Not just yet, not just yet, not just yet, repeated the echoes in the valley, as Luke came out of the cave and saw the Lollybird, a tiny speck, flying farther and farther away over the distant hills.

After this, Luke became very discouraged. He began to feel that he might grow into an old man before the runaway Lollybird decided to come back, that he might as well give up hope of trying to persuade it.

So, very sadly, he went back to the airport and took a plane (he had to charter one specially, for no planes flew that way any more, and this took the last of his money) and he returned to his forest.

The hut was dark and cold, half fallen down, and it was still full of a dreadful tangle of knotted wool and yarn and silk and cotton. Luke was too tired to do anything about the tangle that night, and he had no oil for his lamp, so he lay down in the dark in the middle of it all and went to sleep. But next day he slowly and clumsily set about the disagreeable task of unknotting all the knots and unsnarling all the snarls, winding up all the different lengths of wool and silk, and setting the hut to rights.

But when he had finished it was still

empty and cold and silent. The railway was closed down and grass grew along the track; no planes flew that way any more; winter was coming and the birds were quiet in the forest.

Luke walked slowly through the trees. The silence lay thick as mist.

He remembered how the Lollybird used to fly out with him, looking for plants and mosses.

'Oh,' he cried sadly, 'Oh, how much I miss you, my dearest Lollybird.

He remembered how helpful the Lollybird had always been, and how cheerful, how much it enjoyed inventing new patterns and finding new bits of stuff to weave with, how lively it woke in the mornings, how willingly it worked long hours and how much, when work was done, it had liked to sing its little grating song and pick out a tune on the strings of the mandolin.

'I am sorry I was unkind about its voice,' he thought.

Then he remembered the Lollybird's declaration that it would never return till Luke had found a blue dye in the forest.

'But even if I did find one, how would it ever know?' he thought, and as he wandered along the forest track, tears ran down his face and fell among the withered leaves beside the path.

At last it grew too cold to stay outside any longer, and he went back to the hut.

But, to his astonishment, he saw a light shining in the window. And when he went in, there was his Lollybird. It had lit the lamp, and kindled a little fire, and set a saucepan full of millet porridge on the hob. And it was looking at the empty loom, and the stacked-up shuttles and skeins of wool and yarn, very disapprovingly.

'Am I dreaming?' said Luke. 'Are you a dream, or are you really my Lollybird come back at last?'

'No, I'm not a dream,' said the Lollybird, giving the porridge a stir.

'Oh, my dear friend, my long-lost Lollybird! How very, very glad I am to see you!'

'It's plain I've come back none too soon,' said the Lollybird tartly. 'For you don't appear to have done a stroke of work since I left home.

15

We'd best have our supper quickly and go to bed, for we'll need to get started early in the morning.'

Luke was too happy to ask any questions that night. But, next morning, when they had started work, and the Lollybird was flashing to and fro across the loom with a strand of rose-pink wool in its beak and another under its wing, he did venture to ask timidly,

'I thought you said that you wouldn't come back till I'd found a blue dye in the forest. Why did you change your mind?'

'Oh well,' said the Lollybird, looking down its beak with a casual air, 'if I'd waited for *that*, I've no doubt I'd have had to wait a mighty long time. And to tell the truth I was getting a little bored flying about the world.'

All day they worked, weaving a curtain that was rose-coloured and black and blue and olive-green. When it was done Luke took a thoughtful look at it and said, 'I reckon that's the best bit of work we ever did, my dear Lollybird,' and the Lollybird, also after a careful scrutiny and tweaking all the strands with its beak to make sure that none were loose, replied, 'No, I can't see anything wrong with that little job, master. Who did we make it for?'

'I really forget,' said Luke. 'But I daresay it'll come in handy for something. Now, how about a bit of music?'

He fetched out his old flute and played a tune. And because of its lessons the Lollybird was able to sing him arias from all the greatest operas, in a voice that any nightingale might have envied.

Never again did Luke make his Lollybird work too hard or too long. They took no more orders than would keep them busy for a reasonable part of the day; and when work was over they would go off into the forest, looking for feathers and bright stones, and gaily-coloured leaves.

Next spring, to Luke's astonishment, a new flower came up under the trees, a flower that he had never seen before, which, when picked and dried and powdered, gave them a most beautiful blue dye, a blue as dark and clear as the middle of the ocean on a fine winter day.

'I wonder where the seeds can have come from?' Luke said. 'Maybe some bird dropped them as it flew over. What a mysterious thing!'

But the Lollybird knew that the flowers had sprung up from Luke's tears, as he wandered sadly along the forest path, crying, 'Oh, how very much I miss you, my dearest Lollybird!'

TEN CHARACTERS IN SEARCH
OF A STORY

EDWARD ARDIZZONE

Author and Artist Writes about some of his best-loved books

How time flies! This picture was painted 16 years ago and yet it seems but yesterday. In the picture the old gentleman with a bald head, white hair and dressed in grey is myself. I think I look much the same now though I hope I am just a little slimmer.

Around me are many of the characters I have invented for my books. On my left is Little Tim, the hero of all the Tim books. I hold him by the hand; he is a bit like my son was 40 years ago, a rather solemn little boy with very pale hair. On my right is Lucy Brown. I hold her by the hand too. You cannot see her face in this picture but she looks a bit like my daughter looked when she was 6 years old. She was such a pretty little girl and she liked to wear her blue party frock with lace edges and red ribbons.

Just coming into the picture on the right is Mrs Smawley. Poor Mrs Smawley, how she hated going to sea and how sick she felt! But she was brave. Do you remember how she sat on the hatch cover to prevent the horrible pirate coming out of the hold and how she squashed his fingers? He must have howled with pain.

The old gentleman with a white beard and a yellow hat is old Captain McFee who used to give Tim a sip of his grog, which made Tim want to go to sea more than ever.

Coming in from the left of the picture is Wallis the butcher's errand boy who with his bicycle is often seen near Tim's house by the sea. Behind him the tall boy with gingerish hair and in a yellow pullover is, of course, Ginger.

Now Ginger, next to Tim, is my favourite character, because, like most of us, he was not perfect. Sometimes he was naughty. What trouble he got into when he rubbed the 1st Mate's hair restorer into his head and his hair grew and grew and grew. Also Ginger was sometimes silly and would boast too much, which made further trouble. Above all he was at times a bit of a coward, but once he was very brave and saved Tim's life. He was Tim's best friend.

The girl next to Ginger with the blue bow in her hair is Charlotte, who was washed up by the sea and looked after by Tim and his parents in Tim's house.

Tim and Charlotte became great friends, which made Ginger rather jealous.

Tim was teased by all the other boys at school about his friendship with Charlotte. They used to shout: "Baby Tim loves Charlotte". This made Tim very angry and led to a great fight known for years as "Tim's last stand". Ginger, in spite of being jealous and a bit of a coward, came to Tim's aid and fought bravely beside him.

Of course, having written so many books, there are many of my characters not in this picture. They would not fit in. One of the most important is old Mr Grimes. Talking about him the other day, something strange happened.

I first invented Mr Grimes 40 years ago. Yet only last year I was in the Paddington Recreation Ground, where in my book Mr Grimes used to walk with Lucy, when I saw a sad old man with a great big nose, who looked just like the old man I had invented. I asked the attendant who he was. He answered, "That's old Mr Grimes, he always walks here." His answer, for the moment, made me feel quite queer. Perhaps somebody I had invented had really come alive.

Peter Dickinson creates
IMPOSSIBLE PETS
Visualised by Raymond Briggs

The Cuddlyjob

The Cuddlyjob was soft and small.
It seemed a little limbless ball,
A soft and silky, furry blob—
So Henry bought the Cuddlyjob.

It did not rush about, or spit,
Or hide behind the cupboards. It
Did nothing other creatures do,
With one exception. Yes. It grew.

Within a month that furry scrap
Was far too large for Henry's lap.
Another month, and it no more
Could squeeze itself through any door.

* * * *

Henry is gone. His Mum, his Dad,
The seven sisters that he had—
All gone, and do not ask me where.
But if you should, one evening, care

To bicycle to Henry's street
And then on super-silent feet
As cautious as a hunter, creep
Along the weed-grown path and peep

Through any door or window there
What will you see but silky hair?
One mighty, glossy, furry ball
Filling the house from wall to wall?

(I hope you do not glimpse, beneath
That fur, a gleam . . . that might be . . .teeth.)

The Barracoy

The Barracoy is wild and free.
It will not sit upon your knee
  Nor let you stroke its tempting tum.
In fact, it simply won't pretend
To be your ever-loving friend,
  Nor even purr for milk to Mum.

His Dad bought one for Joseph White
Who did his best to treat it right
  And fed it wildish kinds of meats.
Most nights it slept beneath his bed
But, if it growled and stretched, instead
  He let it out to prowl the streets.

Joseph himself was far from wild,
A sensible and modest child,
  A wholly admirable boy.
But one dull autumn night he caught
His pet's fierce, yellow stare—he thought
  'I wish I were a Barracoy.'

And instantly the thing was so!
The Barracoy turned into Joe—
  Joe's belly changed, to furry white—
His eyes grew yellow, wild and round—
He shook himself—and with one bound
  Leapt out into the wicked night.

Ah, the strange, vivid smells of dark!
The rustling bushes in the park!
  And all along the midnight lanes
Between each lamp a wedge of black
Holding what ambush? What attack?
  Pricked ears, clean muscles, singing veins.

Since then, oh, once a month or so
The Barracoy swaps round with Joe.
  Perhaps one night he'll not return.
His Mum and Dad will watch their boy,
Not guessing it's a Barracoy.

  Some parents have a lot to learn.

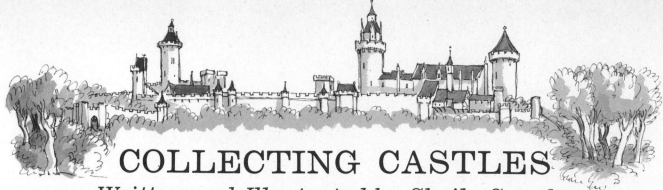

COLLECTING CASTLES
Written and Illustrated by Sheila Sancha

*What I love best in all the
  world
Is a castle, precipice-
  encurled,
In a gash of the wind-
  grieved Appenine . . .*
BROWNING. (*'De Gustibus'*)

Throughout history, people wanted to live in places where they felt secure against attack from unfriendly neighbours. Right back in the misty past, before the Romans came to Britain, Iron Age men built their settlements on natural fortresses: huge cliffs jutting into the sea; islands in the middle of swamps; or remote hills. On the vulnerable sides of the site, they would dig great banks and ditches: the simplest form of defence and splendidly effective.

Some of these ancient sites were abandoned during the Roman occupation of Britain and used again at a later date. The flat-topped hill (*below*) called *South Cadbury Castle* is especially interesting because local tradition says it was Arthur's Camelot.

Not the turreted stone castle of Tennyson's poems, but a wooden fort built sometime round the year A.D. 470 within the Iron Age defences. Of course there's nothing left of this above ground; but part of the site was excavated and traces of post holes found showing wooden ramparts, a gate-tower, and a fair-sized timber feasting hall. So there's a sporting chance that the legend of Camelot really is true.

Castles proper started in Normandy, just before the time of William the Conqueror; but they're difficult to recognize if you're not expecting them. The Normans discovered they could build castles quickly if they dug a circular ditch, lumped the earth into a huge mound at the centre and built a wooden refuge tower on top. The ditch made the mound look twice as high; it's sides were steep and smooth—no chance of a foothold—and from the top the owner of the castle could look out over the trees and see what the enemy was doing. He lived in the 'bailey' alongside and only used the tower when attacked. All the wood having perished, there's usually nothing to look at but the mound and traces of ditches that once surrounded the bailey. However, the tower

was sometimes later replaced by stone walls, and these 'shell keeps' are still there to see.

Enemies were inclined to set fire to wooden castles, so at really important strategic points, stone ones would be built. For those who like the creepy feeling of horrible deeds having been done, then these great square Norman keeps are the goods. Especially on a dark day, when there are no tourists about, and the wind is whistling through the arrow loops.

Other castle addicts prefer to sit in the sun and stare at a heap of stones; putting the building together again in the mind's eye. Here's a romantic ruin:

Château-Gaillard, Richard Coeur de Lion's favourite stronghold.

The best way to attack a castle is to buy a guide book, sit down and read it. Then, with the ground plan firmly fixed in your head, you can march over the

ditch, storm the gatehouse, break into the keep, and feast your eyes on the great hall—where everybody ate and slept. If your history's good enough, you can walk with the ghosts of Kings and Princes.

In England, the most efficient castles were built by Edward 1st. He had trouble with the Welsh, who wanted to keep their own laws and only conquered them by bringing a multitude of masons and labourers in the van of his armies; so they could build strongholds at regular intervals along the coast. If these were cut off by land, the garrison could always get fresh supplies from the sea. King Edward had plenty of ships. When **Harlech Castle** was built on this rock, it overlooked a fine bay; but the water receded and left this area of flat green land. (Right)

King Edward's great seal shows how he looked. He's identified by the arms of England: gules, three lions passant guardent in pale or.

The crusaders built the best castles of all, and the most famous of these is **Crac des Chevaliers**. Originally an Arab stronghold, it was taken, and later—in 1142—handed over to the Knights of St. John, or Hospitallers. These were fighting monks; sworn to protect pilgrims, care for the sick and fight the infidel. Carrying the sword in one hand and the Cross in the other, so to speak. It was a sure passport to Heaven.

These were savage times and they fought in a savage country. Sometimes it was the crusader who was un-horsed. The Saracens had quick-moving ponies and dealt hard blows. They were

a highly civilized people; able to teach the crusaders about honour and courtesy.

Towards the end of the fourteenth century England was anxiously expecting to be invaded by France. French sailors had already swooped across the channel and laid waste the ports of Winchelsea and Rye. So when a knight called Sir Edward Dalyngrigge applied for permission to build a castle, he said it was needed for the defence of the realm. His 'licence to crenellate' was issued in 1385.

The invasion never came; but **Bodiam Castle** was built, and Sir Edward must have been thoroughly proud of it. Not only did the artificial lake and strong walls give him a feeling of security, but the apartments inside were well planned; not jumbled together as in earlier castles, but neatly packed round a courtyard. Apart from the two halls, chapel, store rooms, stables, and kitchens, there were plenty of little rooms with fireplaces where people could be snug and private. The west and north sides, which included the gatehouse, were occupied by the garrison commander and his troops; while the parts of the building shown in this photograph were used by Sir Edward's large household.

In those days people got up with the sun and went to bed when it set. Most of their time was spent outside; hunting in the forest, hawking, training their horses, playing games, having practice jousts and taking part in stately, dangerous tournaments. They enjoyed life to the full, and would often spend the afternoon dancing on the grass, listening to the noisy, boisterous music; or watching a juggler perform his tricks. Minstrels would go from castle to castle, singing songs of Charlemagne and Roland; or—better still—of Arthur. They never envisaged him as a rough chieftain; but always as a splendid medieval king, surrounded by knights just like themselves.

Now that life was getting more comfortable, men as rich as Sir Edward felt they were a cut above eating their meals in a common hall, as their fathers had done. They had separate ones built and feasted well away from the

soldiers and servants. Sir Edward's hall is just behind the tall four-light window in the photograph. It's not so very great, but impressively high: plenty of room for the smoke to curl round the roof beams up above, away from people's eyes. The guests at the high table had some sort of canopy over their heads to protect their fine clothes from the soot. They were careful of their manners; washed before mealtimes, and ate with their fingers and the point of a knife, or a spoon. They could always wipe their greasy hands on a table-cloth. There must have been some memorable meals eaten in that hall, especially at Christmas time.

When he was young, Sir Edward Dalyngrigge had spent much of his time fighting in France. Here's an idea of what he looked like; armed at all points, ready for battle.

Massive walls were easy to destroy once gunpowder had been invented, so any castle built after the fourteenth century is slightly suspect. Places like **Egeskov Castle** were designed more to impress friends than to ward off enemies. This splendid Renaissance building is really a fortified manor house. It was

built about 1550 and its massive weight is supported by over a thousand oak piles, driven into the bed of the lake.

This is a really pompous knight. His armour is specially designed for showing off: to be used at parades and tournaments. Ideal for slow prancing about, but he must have cursed the ostrich feathers in action.

There's a castle to beat all others for sheer good looks. It was built by Ludwig II of Bavaria in 1869. He adored Wagner's operas and got so wrapped up in them that he opted out of political life, forgot to be King, and lived in a dream of people like Tristan and Isolde. **Neuschwanstein Castle** was designed to house them. Inside, the rooms glitter with gold leaf; brilliant, complicated patterns, and forests of candles. The walls are alive with huge paintings of heroes doing deeds of valour. Ludwig felt at home, alone with the ghosts of this chivalric company; but he couldn't afford such extravagant dreams. He ran into debt, his ministers said he had gone completely off his head, and he drowned himself in a romantic lake at the age of 40.

That's Wagner's hero Siegfried (above left), killing the dragon Fafner with his sword Nothung.

LA CORONA AND THE TIN FROG

By Russell Hoban

Illustrated by Fritz Wegner

L A CORONA was the name of the beautiful lady in the picture on the inside of the cigar-box lid. She wore a scarlet robe and a golden crown. Beyond her was a calm blue bay on which a paddle-wheel steamer floated. A locomotive trailed a faint plume of smoke across the pink and distant plain past shadowy palms and pyramids. Far off in the printed sky sailed a balloon.

But the lady never looked at any of those things. She sat among wheels and anvils, sheaves of wheat, hammers, toppled pedestals and garden urns, and she pointed to a globe that stood beside her while she looked steadfastly out past the left-hand side of the picture.

Inside the cigar-box lived a tin frog, a seashell, a yellow cloth tape measure, and a magnifying glass. The tin frog was bright green and yellow, with two perfectly round eyes that were like yellow-and-black bullseyes. He had cost five shillings when new,

had a key in his back, and hopped when wound up. He had fallen in love with La Corona, and he was wound up all the time because of it. He kept trying to hop into the picture with her, but he only bumped his nose against it and fell back into the box.

'I love you,' he told her. But she said nothing, didn't even look at him.

'For heaven's sake!' said the tin frog. 'Look at me, won't you! What do you expect to see out there beyond the left-hand side of the picture?'

'Perhaps a handsome prince,' said La Corona.

'Maybe I'm a prince,' said the tin frog. 'You know, an enchanted one.'

'Not likely,' said La Corona. 'You're not even a very handsome frog.'

'How do you know if you won't look?' said the tin frog. Again he tried to hop into the picture, and again he only bumped his nose and fell back. 'O misery!' he said. 'O desperation!'

'Pay close attention,' said the magnifying glass.

27

'To what?' said the tin frog.

'Everything,' said the magnifying glass. He leaned up against the picture, and the tin frog looked through him. When he looked very close he saw that the picture was made of coloured printed dots. Looking even closer he saw spaces between the dots.

'One doesn't always jump into a picture from the front,' said the magnifying glass.

'Do it by the inch,' said the tape measure.

'Be deep,' said the seashell.

The tin frog thought long and hard. He waited for the moment just between midnight and the twelve strokes of the clock. Everything was dark.

The tin frog dropped the seashell over the side of the cigar-box. He heard a splash. 'Very good,' he said. He unrolled the tape measure over the side of the cigar box. Then he hopped, and found himself in the ocean.

Down, down, down he followed the yellow tape measure in the green and glimmering midnight water. Through coral and sea fans and waving green seaweed he swam, past sunken wrecks and treasures and gliding monsters of the deep, until the tape measure curved up again. Up and up went the tin frog, toward the light, and he came out between the coloured dots of the calm blue bay where the paddle-wheel steamer floated. The dots closed up behind him, and he was in the picture with La Corona.

'Here I am,' said the tin frog when he had swum ashore. 'I love you.'

'You look quite different,' said La Corona. 'You may not be an enchanted prince, but you *are* an enchanting frog.'

They were married soon after that. They took a sea voyage in the paddle-wheel steamer. They drifted far and high across the blue sky in the wicker basket of the balloon. And often they travelled past shadowy palms and pyramids in the train pulled by the locomotive that trailed its faint plume of smoke across the pink and distant plain.

When next the cigar-box was opened it was empty. In the picture on the lid La Corona and the tin frog smiled at each other. And among the wheels and anvils, sheaves of wheat and hammers were the magnifying glass, the tape measure, and the seashell.

You Won't Believe It by Norman Hunter and Peter Edwards

This line . . .

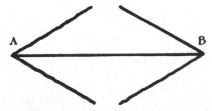

. . . is just as long as this one.

The height of this chap's hat is exactly the same as the width of the brim.

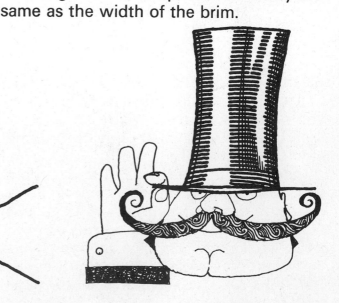

Where was the photographer?

see page 125

HRH Prince Charles The Prince of Wales

The picture that intrigued me when I was small was the "three heads of Charles I" by Sir Antony Van Dyke. In fact it is a portrait of the two profiles of Charles I together with the full face and it hangs at Windsor Castle. Van Dyke painted the King in this way in order to send the picture to Italy where it would act as a model for the famous sculptor, Bernini, to produce a bust of Charles I. The bust has since been destroyed, but the picture remains as an extraordinarily vivid portrayal of the King's features – so vivid that it seems to bring the King back to life and this is the element which makes the picture so fascinating for me. When I was small King Charles lived for me in that room in the castle and I have never forgotten the impression made on me as a result of Van Dyke's supreme skill and sensitivity.

Three Heads of Charles I by Sir Antony Van Dyke
In the collection of HM The Queen
at Windsor Castle

Joyce Grenfell

The Railway Station by W. P. Frith
Royal Holloway College

Pictures that make you think beyond what you are looking at are probably the greatest art, and certainly the most satisfying, but there is also a place for pictures that tell a story and this one by Frith is one of those. People-watching is something I have always enjoyed and that's why Frith's painting pleases me so much. It is full of hurry and bustle and the feelings of coming and going, partings and saying hello. The sweep and rhythm of the composition is exciting. I can even smell the old smoke of coal trains. I'm a glutton for detail. Look at the porters coping with baggage on the *roof* of the train; and at the red-coat lifting up his baby – and the little boy in front gazing with bewilderment at the busy scene. Do you think it's the first time he's ever been to London? When I was a child I used to make up stories about people I saw in trains and buses and you can do that with this picture.

St Jerome in a Rocky Landscape by Joachim Patinir, 16th century.
School of the Antwerp Mannerists

National Gallery, London

34

Yehudi Menuhin

I've always loved this picture because it has so many secret, shadowy corners that one never tires of finding another place where someone might hide and think things out for oneself. I used to believe that that was what St Jerome was up to.

Then what I particularly liked were those strange great rocks that look like cloud formations and the clouds behind them that look like rocks, so that I always felt the whole scene could shift and change, and solid things become vapour and vapour solid. And then there are so many things happening in unexpected corners: strange buildings that seem to have no particular purpose other than to decorate, or perhaps to give a touch of solidity amongst so many uncertain cloud-shapes.

And those strange animals that look like shrunken dinosaurs, or swollen horses, or dotty dromedaries and who either stay there all their lives, or else can somehow reach those stairs, or will perhaps one day simply fall over one of the precipices and land at St Jerome's feet. And those little bits of green to cheer up what would otherwise be a rather chilly ghostscape: the friendly meadow behind the manor house, the distant fields ending a little vaguely in a dark blue sea, the sparse trees clinging determinedly to those great pale blue crags, and the little glimpse of sunlit plain with its cottages on the right hand side, looking quite ordinary and everyday in contrast to the rest of the sculptured, dreamy, unreal landscape.

And what is the old fellow doing clambering up that staircase coming from nowhere and going to nowhere, with his stick oddly in his *left* hand and his little dog bounding ahead of him? That staircase *must* lead to the manor house . . . and yet? You can search and travel and invent stories about this picture for ever and ever.

P.S. There are very few Patinir paintings in the world, but there is a beautiful one in all colours of red called "Sodom and Gomorrah" at the Ashmolean Museum in Oxford and several in the Prado Gallery in Madrid.

Two's Company

by Norman Hunter and
Peter Edwards

A nonsense page of tricks and questions

How to Make Money

You count four coins onto the open pages of a book and pour them into a basin.

'This,' you say, 'is a special kind of cookery book. It has a recipe for making money multiply.'

You tip the coins out of the basin and the audience see that there are now eight coins instead of four.

To do this choose a book that is thick enough to take a two penny piece down inside the binding at the back of the book. Put four two penny pieces into the binding and close the book. You can handle the book freely and the coins will not fall out.

In performing the trick, open the book about the middle and lay it on the table. Count four two penny pieces onto the open pages. Now pick up the open book and pour the coins into a basin. The book being open, the binding at the back will be loose and the four hidden coins will fall into the basin with the others.

How the four coins are hidden in the binding of the book.

The hidden coins fall out of the binding into the basin with the other coins.

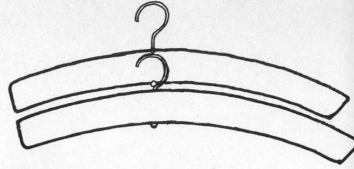

Would you believe that . . .
These coat hangers are both exactly the same size.

Sort This Lot Out

You have ducks in cricket, birdies in golf; what do you have in bowls?

Answer: Soup.

Think of two coins amounting to two and a half new pence. One of them must not be a half new penny.

Answer: a two penny piece and a half penny piece. (One of the coins must not be a half penny piece but the other may be.)

A man gave up watching comedians on television and watched lady magicians instead. What would he be doing?

Answer: Going from wags to witches.

If ten flies alighted on a table and you killed one, how many would be left?

Answer: None, they would be all right.

If you are walking down a road and you come to a dead end, what do you do?

Answer: Stop dead.

HOW BIRDS FLY

Charles Gibbs-Smith gives us some surprising and little known information.　　**drawings by Jill McDonald**

Until the early years of the twentieth century, it was universally believed that birds 'swim' through the air as a man swims in water. In his famous notebooks, the artist Leonardo da Vinci stated this belief explicitly, referring, of course, to the action of the man's arms. But, in fact, a bird cannot beat its wings downwards and backwards, and it would capsize if ever it did.

The basic method of all bird and bat propulsion is the 'propellering' action of the outer parts of the wings, *the wing-ends*, with either the whole of each wing twisting at the end into a shape similar to an airscrew, or each of the outer primary feathers twisting separately into individual 'airscrews'.

Most of the forward thrust of a bird's wings is exerted on the downstroke, which produces both a lift and major thrust acting forwards (horizontally), the latter being increased in proportion to the amount of twist occurring in the wing-ends or in the separated primary feathers. On the up-stroke, no lift is produced, but still some propulsion.

So nature has here produced two 'half-propellers', so to speak, instead of one complete rotating propeller, since in nature there is seldom—if ever—to be found any kind of rotary motion.

In birds, this 'propellering' process occurs only in the outer parts of the wings, because they develop the necessary high speed properly to engage the air; whereas the inner parts of the wings move much more slowly—too slowly to affect the air—and produce the major part of the bird's lift.

But the bird itself does not initiate the twisting process of its wings; all the twisting is done aerodynamically by their motion through the air. So it is the air pressure itself which produces the twisting of the wings.

This 'propellering' of a bird's wings is achieved in four basically different ways, according to the type of wing.

(**1**) In some birds with very low aspect-ratio wings —i.e. short broad wings— and wings which are 'floppy', a large amount of each whole wing twists *up-wards* into a propeller as the wing is beaten downwards. This is also how bats propel themselves.

(**2**) With other types of stiffer, low aspect-ratio wings, there are generally about five outer primary feathers which stick out from the broad end of the wing, at right angles to the body. When beaten down, the rear surface of the wing is forced up, and the feather twists into a propelling airscrew as it is beaten down. The five or so feathers stand well clear of one another, and amount to being five propellers on the *down-stroke*; but they are slightly less effective on the *up-stroke*, in which the rear vanes are forced downwards. In gliding and soaring flight, these feathers are held out rigid; they then amount to five small high aspect-ratio wings, i.e. long and narrow, and they are particularly useful for the control of the bird at slow speeds, and can, it is believed, delay any stalling of the wings which may tend to set in.

(**3**) In many smaller birds,

with low (or moderate) aspect-ratio wings, there also occur these special feathers; but they are set closer together and are much larger in relation to the wing as a whole, and hence act as more efficient high-speed propellers.

(4) Then there are the birds with long narrow wings whose primary feathers do not separate to act as propellers, in whom the whole end of each wing twists up collectively behind, as the wing is beaten down. Here the wings are, so to speak, hinged to a front spar, and flap upwards when the spar beats down. In some of these birds it is possible that the whole end of the wing can also be slightly flexed backward in flapping flight to make the bird's 'hand' flap up and down from the wrist, and so produce the same effect.

When flying normally in a level flight-path, a bird simply flaps its wings up and down, with the airscrew ends propelling it through the air, and their mere motion downwards and forwards (as the bird travels forwards) also pro-

A Gannet stretches its feet and fans its wings and tail as it prepares to land.

ducing a thrust component. It is in high-speed multiple photographs of such normal flying that the wing-ends appear well in front of the wing-roots— indeed in front of the bird's body at times—at the bottom of the down-stroke. This movement forwards, as well as downwards, is again not 'intended' by the bird: it is simply the result of the propelling tips pulling the wing-ends forward, and, with them, the whole bird itself. The photographs also reveal what is in effect an overall figure-of-eight movement of the wing-tips. This again is not the bird's 'intention'. When the tips are far advanced at the end of the down-stroke, they are simply raised by the bird's muscles to the up-position. In getting to this position the wings must swing both backwards and upwards at the same time. Then, when the next down-stroke is made, the propelling tips take them both forwards and downwards. The result is a figure-of-eight tracing of the whole combined up-and-down beat of the wings in which the bird has simply beaten

An Antarctic Petrel glides peacefully along, seemingly without effort.

its wings straight up and down and the aerodynamic forces acting on them have taken them through the figure-of-eight course.

The Secret of Helicoptering

From what has been said, it may readily be seen that if a bird rears up its body so that it is almost 'standing' in mid-air, and continues to beat its wings up and down, the thrust exerted by the wings is now acting *upwards*, and the bird is therefore 'helicoptering'. Almost all birds use this technique when they come in to land, just before they actually touch down: with their tail spread wide and drawn downwards as an airbrake, and their wings helicoptering, they can come to a halt exactly on the chosen landing spot.

But some birds can also swivel their wings at the roots, and beat them more or less forwards and backwards without rearing their bodies up very much, in order to obtain the same results as before.

A bird can also swivel its wings to alter the angle at which they beat; it can also beat them at varying speeds; and it can beat one

continued on page 43

A puffin coming in to land. Its body is reared up, and its wings beating obliquely, and from back to front provide upward (helicoptering) thrust as well as horizontal thrust, ensuring good lift at slow speeds. Its sparse little tail is drawn down to form an air-brake, and the feet extended ready for landing.

A puffin in the act of touching down, with its reared-up body and its wings beating from back to front, generating maximum upward thrust for the last seconds of landing. Its tail is still down in the air-brake position, but now closed.

Two swans during their take-off run. The swan has such a high wing-loading (i.e. heavy weight in relation to the wing area) that it must run and skitter along the surface of the water until its forward speed is great enough to generate sufficient lift in the wings to allow the bird to become airborne.

A golden eagle hovering. This regal bird has low aspect-ratio wings and clearly separated outer primary feathers which form five miniature wings; this enables the eagle to maintain full flight-control at high angles of incidence and postpone any tendency for such broad wings to stall. It is here seen using its half-spread tail as its main control surface, now swivelled to effect a rudder action.

The superb appearance of a flamingo in full flight. When properly airborne, it stretches its neck out front to balance its exceptionally long 'undercarriage' which is drawn up and is held out rigidly at the back, thus keeping the bird's centre of gravity approximately amidships.

A gannet snapped in mid-flight, and at the start of the down-stroke of its wings. The black parts can already be seen twisting up at the back to provide the thrust component of its flight. The narrow tail is here seen pulled down into the position of an air-brake.

The beautiful and almost incredible humming bird, with its ultra-rapid wing-beat, and the unique ability to fly backwards in order to disengage its beak from the flower. The absence of wing covert feathers over the wing-roots allows the wings to be swivelled round and thus provide reverse thrust. In its reared-up position the wings beat from back to front to provide vertical thrust, like a helicopter, in order that the bird can keep stationary in front of the flower.

wing slower or faster than the other, in order to assist in a sharp turn.

The only known bird that can stay in the same spot when flying in still air, and even fly backwards, is the humming bird. Its wings, unlike other birds', are free to swivel right round in their root-sockets; this allows it to 'helicopter' whilst keeping its beak inside a flower; then to swivel them even further round, at which the bird will still be producing enough upward thrust to

SOME CALL IT AERODYNAMICS I CALL IT SWANK

keep on a level flight-path and also enough rearward thrust to pull back out of the flower; finally, the bird reverses its wing-swivelling, its body sinks into a horizontal position for normal flight, and off it flies.

The tail of most birds, which is kept closed in straight fast flight, can be spread, closed, or swivelled —at lightning speed—to aid, manoeuvring when gliding or flying slowly. The bird can also close one side of the tail more or less than the other. Much of a bird's steering is done by spreading and swivelling the tail, as you can see if you watch pigeons. The tail, when spread, can add greatly to the overall area and hence to the lift of the bird at slow speeds, and can also act as an air-brake when spread and pulled down.

Taking-off and Landing

When taking-off, a bird with a low wing-loading (i.e. large wings and light body) may give a hop so it can get in its first wing-beats, or just take straight off if it has long legs. If it has a high wing-loading (i.e. small wings in relation to its body weight) like a duck, goose, or swan, it must skitter on its feet along the surface of the water until its forward speed is great enough to produce lift on the wings for complete take-off. A bird will always take off and land into wind when possible.

When landing, all birds manoeuvre so that they approach the landing area into wind; when banking,

The old problem of how a fly lands on the ceiling — previously thought to have been by means of a half-roll — has now been finally settled. The fly, on nearing the ceiling with the intention of landing, zooms vertically upwards and thrusts forward the front pair of its six sucker-feet until they impact on the ceiling; its body is then carried on and upwards by centrifugal force until the other four sucker-feet impact the ceiling and adhere to it.

all birds twist their necks to keep their heads level with the ground, and, as they approach the ground or water, they rear up to present their wings at a greater angle or beat their wings forwards to get upward thrust; they will simultaneously spread and pull down their tails to act as airbrakes, and put down their legs. Small birds, and birds with a high

wing-loading, beat their wings all the way down, and, as they rear up, their wings are helicopering to produce thrust upwards.

DRATTED HITCH-HIKERS

DOVER

When gliding and soaring, most birds can sweep their wings forward or backward, or flex them to any degree, thus altering the centre of pressure for climbing or diving, and reducing the effective wing-area for fast glides and other manoeuvres. Both dihedral and anhedral wing positions are employed when gliding and soaring.

Larger birds always fly in a formation, so designed that it avoids the birds being upset by flying through the turbulent air left by those in front; these formations can be of various kinds such as a V, echelon to port or starboard, line abreast, line astern (stepped up or down), and so on.

No words can do justice to the bird's superb and sensitive control of its flying apparatus. Certain insects possess an even more extraordinary power of flight, and the aerodynamics of such a creature as the dragonfly, which can pass instantaneously from stationary to highspeed flight in any direction— and vice versa—are little short of miraculous.

Tale The Second

THE TIN HORSEMAN
By Russell Hoban

Illustrated by Fritz Wegner

THE weather castle was printed on a card that hung by the window. It stood on a rocky island in the middle of a bright blue sea, and coloured banners flew from the tops of its tall towers. When the weather was fair the rocky island was blue. When rain threatened the island turned purple, and when the rain fell the island was pink.

The tin horseman lived on a shelf near the window. He had a pale heroic face. He wore a yellow fringed Indian suit and a headdress of red feathers. His dapple-grey horse had a red saddle-cloth. They had been stamped from a sheet of tin, printed on one side only, and shaped in a mould so that they had some form to them.

Long ago there had been a flat tin clown, a red-and-yellow magnet, and two or three coloured rings with the horseman. Now he was alone. Day after day he looked at the little windows of the weather castle, and he was certain that he had seen the face of a beautiful yellow-haired princess at one of them.

'When the island is blue I shall gallop there and find her,' he said. But when the island was blue he did not gallop to the castle, because he was afraid.

The tin horseman was afraid of the little round yellow glass-topped box that was the monkey game of skill. Inside it crouched the monkey, printed on a yellow background. He had a horrid pink face, and empty holes where his eyes belonged. His eyes were silver balls that had to be shaken into place.

The tin horseman was afraid that when the monkey had his eyes in place he might do dreadful things, and he was sure that the monkey was skilful enough to shake them into place whenever he wanted to. The monkey lived between the tin horseman and the castle, and the tin horseman never dared to gallop past.

Day after day he looked at the castle windows, and daily he became more certain that he saw the yellow-

44

haired princess. Once he thought she even waved her hand to him. 'When the island is pink I shall gallop there,' he said. 'One rainy day I shall smash the glass and throw away the monkey's silver eyes and ride to the princess.' But he was afraid, and stayed where he was, dusty on the shelf.

One night, just between midnight and the twelve strokes of the clock, words came to the tin horseman: 'Now or never.' He didn't know whether he had heard them or thought them, but his fear left him, and in the dim light from the window he spurred his horse toward the weather castle and the princess of his dreams.

Just as he was passing the monkey game of skill he was surrounded by complete darkness. All was black, and he could see nothing. Again words came to him: 'Fear is blind, but courage gives me eyes.' And again the tin horseman did not know where the words came from nor why he did what he did next.

He dismounted, and felt in the dark for the monkey game of skill. He remembered his thought of smashing the glass and throwing away the eyes, but he did not do that. He shook it gently. One, two, he heard the eyes roll into place. He closed his eyes and waited.

A golden glow came from the glass top of the box, and seeing the glow through his closed eyelids he opened his eyes. The monkey was gone. There in the golden light stood the yellow-haired princess he had longed for. She was not in the weather castle, but here before him.

'Your courage has broken my enchantment,' she said. 'There is a sorcerer who lives in the weather castle. It was he who wanted you to smash the glass and throw away the monkey's eyes, and if you had done that I should have been lost to you forever.'

'Now I *will* ride to the castle,' said the tin horseman. He pried the glass top off the box and took the princess up on his horse. Over the blue sea they galloped, straight to the island and across the drawbridge to the castle. The castle was empty. The sorcerer had fled.

After that the tin horseman and the princess lived in the weather castle with the coloured banners flying from the towers, while the island turned blue or pink or purple as the weather changed.

But the glass was back on top of the little round yellow box that had been the monkey game of skill. From then on someone else lived there, and no one ever looked to see who it might be.

A nervous young lady of Bicester
Went out with a fellow, who kicester.
She squirmed in his clutch
And wriggled so mutch
It took several weeks to untwicester.

PYAW

BLIMEY!! TURN DOWN THE SMELL

A violinist who played on the telly
Compounded a curious jelly.
It gave strength to the ahms
For the playing of Brahms,
But the stuff was infernally smelly.

ENGLAND IS A PALIMPSEST

Jill Paton Walsh suggests some clues to help you read the landscape, illustrated with painting by Anthony Colbert from *The Changing Face of England* by Edward Hyams

Long ago, when books were written out by hand, they were written on specially prepared leather—parchment or vellum—made from the skins of calves or sheep or goats, and whitened and smoothed, and this stuff, while very beautiful, was so expensive that sometimes it got used more than once, when an old book wasn't wanted any more, or the need for a new book was very great, the ink letters were scraped off the skin with a sharp knife, the surface was burnished smooth again and the pages were written over a second time.

Of course it was impossible to get the page absolutely clean; almost always it is possible to discern the faint shadow left by the old letters. It shows in the spaces between lines, or the gaps between words. And very often the rubbed-out writing seems more interesting to modern people than the second text written over the top, so that they spend lots of time and care trying to make out the rubbed-out words. A twice-used page like this is called a 'palimpsest'.

Well, the whole of England is a palimpsest. Of course it's been used more than twice—it's been used in hundreds of different ways, and the more recent ways overlay and hide most of the earlier ones. But it's absolutely astonishing how indelible marks on the landscape are. There are always gaps and spaces, in which the ghosts of older 'words' show faintly through. Just dig a hole and fill it in again, and in a thousand years there on that particular spot the grass will be greener, the corn just slightly higher. Archaeologists, willing to dig again, can find and detect all

sorts of vanished detail. If they find post holes that took the wooden pillars in an Anglo-Saxon hall, by checking how deep the hole was dug, they can work out how high the roof was and even how thick the post was, by examining the infilling of the hole (the little avalanches of pebbles that rattled into it from the rim, and came to rest against the wooden post). At Fishbourne they have found the bedding trenches dug to make a Roman garden, and have replanted the garden in the same rather formal pattern.

Actually, digging is rather like clearing away the second layer of writing to see the first one better, and the digging itself leaves its own mark behind it. Sometimes, too, the 'writing over the top' was not boring or valueless. And for me, if you strip the thing down, and leave only one level clear, it loses half its fun.

I like palimpsests better than clean once-and-for-all manuscripts, and landscapes better when, without lifting a spade or a shovel, but just with a keen and curious eye, I can make out more than one layer at once. Looking from a train, for example, seeing the green undulating surface of cornfields, suddenly there is a field in which the silken bumps have a pattern, a jumble of rectangles—and you can guess that there, beneath next winter's growing bread, lie houses—a deserted village, forgotten streets. Look carefully, and you will see nearby fields like corrugated paper, grooved for a millenium by the plough pattern of those villagers.

Or you might notice that an unimportant seeming footpath keeps in an unwavering, steady line from

parish to parish, at the same distance down from the brow of the hill. That track is very likely older than the parish itself. One of the odder things about all this is how the clearness with which we can read an older sign bears no relation to the age of it. Beside that village, faintly visible as a cropmark, or the frowning pasture whose wrinkles remember being a field, how startlingly clear the Stone Age can be; vastly older, but showing through in great standing stones, and immense earthworks, still as clear to the eye as when they were new—just softened a bit.

How odd that those ancient people should have marked England so much more deeply than the Romans—really you can only see the Romans as straight lines on a map; or from a hilltop where, perhaps, you can see a road that seems to have been made by laying down a ruler.

The Anglo-Saxons really covered the page, instead of just dotting it—really took possession of the land. Field, meadow, ploughland, pasture, the siting of the villages, and the outlying farms, and most of the names we call them by, all

belong to this 'text'. You can read, slurred over a bit, on signposts all over England the names of the men who first made farms and villages, and clues, too, on how they did it. 'Godalming' means 'Godhelm's people', 'Finchingfield' means 'The field of Finc's people'. Barnet and Swithland were cleared of trees by burning . . .

And yet more interesting still, I think, is the sight that brings home to us how our age too will be a rapidly fading scar. . . Motorways are too new to be fading yet; but from the trains you can often see a derelict branch line forking to left or right. The rails have been taken up for scrap, the sleepers for firewood, grass covers the gravel bed,

but the trace of that line, growing fainter and fainter, will never be entirely lost . . . and one day, doubtless, even the motorway will be only a long scar running beneath the grasses and the great ugly coal mines will be grassy hollows in pitted fields . . . and the surface will be ready to be used again.

In the beginning the 'blank page' was covered by great oak forests (above). Much later, man began to make his impact on the land. The Windmill Hill

people (above left), who developed farming, social organisation and the domestication of animals left great cattle-corrals and the famous 'long barrows' behind them. The Saxons covered the page with their formal settlements (left) and farms. By the fifteenth century these early settlements had either developed into thriving communities or been overlaid with a pattern of fields and hedgerows as the great age of enclosed farming arrived (below).

Walter & His Magic
by Mel Calman

Walter wanted to do magic. So he bought a magic stick. He waved it over his cat.

'Become a lion,' he ordered. But his cat just sat there and did not even blink – let alone become a lion.

So Walter bought a magic hat and a magic cloak. 'Become a lion,' he said again. The cat smiled and said, 'Shan't.'

'I will try once more,' said Walter. He bought a pair of magic shoes from the best magic shop in town.

'Become a lion,' said Walter. And to Walter's amazement the cat slowly, slowly . . .

changed into a real lion.

Walter was completely surprised. And so was the cat.

And then the lion opened his huge mouth and ate Walter all up – magic stick, hat, cloak and shoes as well.

Moral : Be careful what you want – you may get it.

48

THE BOY, THE DOG AND THE SPACESHIP

by NICHOLAS FISK

There was a boy and his dog, running and rolling and chasing in a field.

✧ ✧ ✧ ✧ ✧

There was a spaceship hurtling through nothingness, most of its crew already dead, and the rest despairingly fighting on to make landfall on a strange planet.

✧ ✧ ✧ ✧ ✧

The boy's name was Billy. He was nine. His dog was called Scamp. He was young too. Boy and dog understood each other perfectly.

Billy shouted 'Devil dog!' and pounced at Scamp. Scamp rolled his eyes, yelped with delight and pranced off sideways. Billy chased Scamp until he was tired out. Then they sat down together, side by side in the evening shadows. When they had got their breath back, Billy shouted 'Devil dog!' and the chase started all over again.

✧ ✧ ✧ ✧ ✧

In the spaceship, the Captain contacted the Engineer. The channel was live—the Captain could hear the slight echoing hiss from the speaker—yet the Engineer did not respond.

The Captain barked, 'Report. I want your report. Make your report.'

The Engineer's breathing changed. It turned into long sobs. '*Report.*'

The Engineer spoke. 'It's no good, Captain, it's no good . . .! The heat's burned out the bounce beam, the retros have gone dead. We'll just hit, Captain. We're going to smash.

Seconds later, the retros bellowed and the ship checked so violently that the Captain fell over. He got up bleeding. He said, 'Engineer!' then noticed the Engineer's light had died which meant that the Engineer had died. So he called the In-Flight Tech.

'In-Flight, we have full retro, am I correct?'

'Eighty per cent retro, Captain. No more to come. But it may be enough –'

'It must be enough.'

'Yes, Captain.'

'Very well. Crashball, In-Flight. And tell the others.'

'The others,' the Captain said to himself. 'Just two others . . .'

He switched off and began to fit himself into the crashball cocoon. He fitted webbing harnesses over his body and buckled them. He pressed a button and padded arms enfolded him. A little tubular snake leapt from a padded hole and latched itself to a socket near his neck: his clothing began to swell, then the walls of the cocoon. The puffed surfaces met. Now he was completely encased in a puffy softness, pressing tighter and tighter.

He waited for the stab. It came. The needle darted itself into one of the Captain's veins. A drug entered his bloodstream. Almost immediately he felt drowsy and comfortable, but still alert. The same needle was connected to a whole junction of tiny tubes filled with his own blood and plasma; with stimulants, painkillers, curatives and other life givers and life adjusters; even with painless death.

'Check in,' said the Captain.

The In-Flight Tech and the Co-ordinator should have answered. Their lights were live. The Co-ordinator said, 'Excuse me, Captain, but I think I'm dying.' A moment later he died.

'In-Flight Tech,' said the Captain.

No answer.

'In-Flight Tech! Check in!'

'Yes, Captain?'

'Just checking,' said the Captain, and switched off so that the Tech should not hear his sigh of relief.

The ship hurtled on. It was still slowing, the Captain could feel it through the cocoons. In the control centre, the screens showed a green and blue planet with seas and clouds and land masses, coming nearer all the time. But there was no-one outside the cocoons to watch the screens.

The boy whistled for his dog. 'Here boy!' he commanded, and whistled again. 'Come on, Scamp!'

Scamp pranced and curvetted towards the boy, being silly. He wanted to make the boy laugh, but the boy was solemn. He was proud of having such a well trained dog. 'Good boy,' he said gravely, 'Good old Scamp.'

A minute later, the boy and the dog were wrestling in the grass.

The ship entered Earth's atmosphere. Its metal skin now drove against air instead of nothingness. The ship screamed. Its metal skin changed colour and in places glowed dull red with the heat.

The In-Flight Tech's cocoon shifted, tearing from its framing. A cluster of tiny tubes pulled away from a socket, away from the needle. Blood, drugs squirted uselessly. The In-Flight Tech died without a word.

The Captain watched his light go out and said, 'All right. All right. Alone. I'll do it alone.'

They stopped their wrestling match and looked about them.

'You heard it! It went sort of *whee-oosh*,' Billy said to Scamp. '*Wheeeee-oooosh*.' Scamp flicked his head sideways to acknowledge his master's words, but went on staring at the dark corner of the trees. Scamp had heard the noise. He didn't know where it came from, but he knew where it led. He marked the place in his nose and mind. Over there, by the dark trees.

'So that's what it's like,' said the Captain. He had never before experienced a smash landing. He had to say something, even if there was no-one to hear him. He kept his voice level.

He waited for the needle to deliver whatever his body needed. While he waited, he disciplined his mind and made it think and plan.

'Conquest,' this mind said. 'I am alone, but I am still here as a conqueror. I will conquer this planet.'

'Method,' he continued. 'I am alone; but usual procedure will be followed. I will find a creature of the planet. I will invade its mind: make it obey me. I will then make all creatures of its kind obey the creature I inhabit.'

'Having conquered one creature and one species, I will move on, always seeking the higher creatures. If there is a ruling species on this planet, I will invade a creature of that species and thus become ruler of all.'

He pressed the Release Control. The halves of the cocoon opened.

The new conqueror of the planet Earth flexed his limbs, tested his organs and senses, opened the main doors and stepped forth.

Billy pretended not to hear his mother's call, but then decided to obey. A long way away, right at the edge of the field, he could see the yellow glimmer of the lamp on her bicycle. 'Oh lor,' he thought, 'she's had to get on the bike to come after me. She won't be pleased . . .' To the dog, he said, 'Come on, Scamp. Come on, boy!' But Scamp was running back and forth by the dark trees.

'Bill-eeeee!' his mother shouted. 'You come home now, or I'll – '

'It's Scamp, *he* won't come!' shouted Billy furiously.

And he wouldn't. Billy could see Scamp running up and down, doing a sort of sentry duty on the trot by the edge of the trees. The dog's ears were pricked, his tail was high, his body alert. He wouldn't obey.

The Captain's helmet indicators read SAFE, so the planet's air was breathable. Nevertheless, he kept his helmet on. He was glad to be protected with helmet and armour. He was grateful to the brains and skills that had designed his armoured suit and given him a strength greater than his own. The Captain could clench a hand—and the suit's own metal hand would clench with such force that it could crush metal. The Captain was strong and fit—but his suit was tireless and inexhaustible. If the Captain's nerves, muscles and movements said 'run', the suit would run endlessly. If the Captain's body said 'climb', the suit would keep climbing for him.

Now was the time, the Captain realized, to climb.

He had seen many worlds, explored many planets. He had never seen one like this. This world was bursting with life. From the corner of his eye, the Captain saw something move, very fast, on several legs. Above him, something flew. Behind him, something scurried. He was not in the least surprised. How could there fail to be active, animal life in so rich a place?

Climbing was what mattered now. He had to get on and up. Where he stood, he was completely surrounded and blinded by vegetable richness. Great green ribbed things, taller than the highest mountains of his own planet, reached indefinitely upwards —no, not indefinitely, he could see dark blue sky still further above. A vast green trunk sprang from the soil very near him. It was the right size and shape and it had projections: ideal for climbing. He clasped his limbs round this trunk. The suit took over and climbed him towards the dark blue sky, away from the ship with its hideous cargo of broken bodies; and from the stench of death.

At first, there had just been a faint whiff of it. Now, it was a full-bodied and glorious stench—better still, a new stench! Scamp's black nostrils widened still further. There! Over there! He gave a stifled yelp of ecstasy as the smell strengthened; he bounded towards it.

'Billy!' said his mother. 'Never mind the dog, you come home and eat your supper. Come on, now! I'm not waiting a moment longer!'

51

Billy stopped and gave one last yell. 'Scamp! Scaaaaamp!'

Scamp did not hear. Only tracking down the smell mattered.

The Captain could climb no higher. The green column that supported him was bending and swaying under his weight. He wrapped his limbs round the column and felt the suit lock itself securely into position. He looked around him.

He was in a dense forest of green columns, all very much the same as the one he had climbed yet each different. A few were rod-like (his column was ribbed and almost flat). Some columns carried grotesque explosions of strange branching shapes on their heads. A great nest of columns in the distance supported flat, outward-branching green platforms and—amazing!—complicated crown-shaped yellow platforms at their summits.

He adjusted his helmet to take in air from the outside. The air was moist, perfumed, sumptuous. He let the helmet supply his mouth with a sample of the moisture that was making droplets over everything; the water was cold, clean, simple, almost certainly safe—and absolutely delicious. On his own planet, he had tasted such air and water only in the laboratories. Reluctantly, he returned to the closed-circuit environment of his suit and helmet . . .

An amazing planet! A planet of limitless, unending, inexhaustible richness! And he was to be its conqueror. The thought was stunning. For once, the Captain allowed himself simply to feel pleasure: to stare at nothing and to dream of glory.

Here! Scamp's nose was actually touching the wonderful source of the supreme stench!

He licked the source of the smell. It was cold and dewy and hard. He had expected something still warm, still half alive, still rubbery-soft; it was that sort of smell. But perhaps the cold, hard outer case was only a container, like the tube of bone that encloses the marrow? Carefully, he opened his mouth and picked up the container thing in his jaws. Nothing happened, so he put it down again, holding it between his front paws, and looked at it with his head on one side.

It seemed harmless. He lowered his head, opened his jaws and bit.

The Captain saw a monster.

Once the terror and shock were over there were three things to be done (Past, Present and Future, as the training manuals put it). First, understand exactly what had happened—the Past; second, make up your mind what immediate action to take—Present; third, decide what advantage could be gained by further action—Future.

All right. Past. He had seen the monster—a living thing, not a machine—travel at incredible speed, crash through the green columns and spires, trampling them flat in its haste. The monster was white, brown and black and ran on legs. It had made straight for the crashed ship. When the monster's face opened, it was pink inside and had pointed white mountains above and below.

The monster had done various things, that the Captain could not see, to the ship. Finally it had picked up the ship, holding it between the white mountains, and crushed it. The Captain had heard the metal screech.

All right. Now the Present.

The body of the monster must be entered by the Captain so that the Captain could take it over in the usual way. He had to get nearer the monster. That should be easy enough provided that the monster did not suddenly go away on its big legs.

Finally, the Future.

Well, that was obvious enough, thought the Captain. Follow the normal procedure. Invade the monster's brain and gain control of its body and its actions.

After that, the invasion would follow its normal course. All species—high or low—would eventually obey the Captain. By then the Captain would have contacted his home planet. More ships would come bearing settlers. At last the Captain's race would have found a safe, fitting, rich and permanent home.

He went towards the monster.

Billy picked at his supper, but his mother said, 'Do eat up!' and watched him until he finished every morsel. He didn't want food. He wanted Scamp.

His mother said, 'And do your homework.' She bustled out of the room. A minute or so later, he heard the T.V. She liked that programme, she never missed it! And she wouldn't miss *him*.

He tiptoed to the back door, opened it silently, closed it silently, and was on his way to the big field.

The Captain was within reach. The white parts of the monster glowed pale but clear in the failing light. The Captain muttered 'Climb'. The suit took him up fast.

The Captain had chosen a green spire to climb—a flat-sided spire that would bend when he reached the top of it. The monster was not moving. It was crouched over the remains of the ship. 'Climb. Climb . . .'

Just as he reached the right place and was about to sway the tip of his spire towards the monster, the monster moved! The Captain made a split-second decision and leaped into nothingness. He stretched his limbs—clutched—and held. Victory!

Gripping one cluster of white or brown or black rods after another, the Captain clambered his way along the monster, making for the brain. It was above the monster's face. He could feel the brain's energy.

He came to the entrance of a tunnel leading into the monster's head and smiled. He clambered into the tunnel, the suit making light work of the journey. Now the brain signals were deafening—even the helmet was overwhelmed. The Captain turned back. He made himself comfortable outside the entrance of the tunnel, anchoring himself securely. He checked some readings and responses. Good. The monster was hearing him.

'You'll enjoy this,' the Captain told the monster. 'You'll like obeying me. You'll like the things we do. You *will* obey me, won't you? Of course you will. You *will* obey me, always . . .'

Billy found Scamp. At first he was glad to find him, but very soon he was puzzled. He kept shaking his head, and he was running. 'He's got a burr in his ear,' thought Billy. 'Or an insect. An itch.'

Scamp was running in regular patterns—a straight line, a pause, a turn to the left, then another straight line, then a pause and a turn to the right. It looked weird in the moonlight. Billy began to be frightened.

Then Scamp suddenly sat down, some ten yards away, and looked straight at Billy. The dog did not move a muscle. He just stared.

The Captain halted the monster—the up-and-down motion of the monster's running disturbed his thought—and thought very carefully.

'The monster is a servant creature,' he decided. 'And the upright monster, the one that just arrived, is a superior creature because he makes audio signals and expects them to be obeyed. How do I know that? Because when the upright monster made his signals, my monster was uneasy. He tried to disobey me.' The Captain smiled a little at the thought.

'But does it matter which monster is the master?' he thought. Probably not. They are both much the same size. If they fought, who knows which would win?

'Not that *that* matters much either,' thought the Captain. 'Because I am the controlling brain. So I could appoint either as the master species of the planet. Nevertheless . . .'

Billy shouted 'Scamp! Come here when I call you!' But Scamp just sat there in the moonlight, staring straight at him, motionless.

Billy said—this time almost pleading—'Come on, boy. Good boy. Come on Scamp. Please.'

But the dog just stared and his eyes looked strange in the moonlight.

'Nevertheless,' thought the Captain,

Drawings by John Vernon Lord.

'It might be as well to find out which is master. Besides, one or the other of them might have powerful weapons I should know about. I'll try it.'

He spoke to the dog's brain.

'Kill,' said the Captain. 'Kill that other creature there.'

The dog attacked. 'Scamp!' yelled Billy. 'Don't, Scamp!'

Scamp over-ran him and turned and charged again, snarling like a hound of hell. And then the dog had hurtled the boy to the ground and was standing over him, jaws open, teeth bared.

'SCAMP!' It was a scream of terror.

The dog paused. The big voice in his head said 'KILL!' but the old, loved, familiar voice was calling too, asking for help.

The dog paused; the boy struck out blindly with his fist. He hit the dog's ear. Something small fell to the ground, unseen. The little thing was mortally wounded. It writhed.

Scamp said 'Woof!' in a vague way and looked at Billy. The dog licked the boy's face, wagged his tail and sheepishly got off Billy's chest. He sat down and scratched his ear with a hind paw. But the itching had gone.

The little, unseen thing writhed for the last time; and, hidden in the grass, the Captain died.

The boy and the dog rollicked off together across the moonlit field. Sometimes the boy chased the dog: sometimes the dog chased the boy. When they got home, they were both scolded by Billy's mother.

By the edge of the trees, the dew was heavy on the spaceship. Soon it would rust and become as brown as the earth. But now it was still shiny and glinting in the tall weeds. In the moonlight, you wouldn't have noticed where its body was crushed and dented. It looked like a super-perfect model. Little, but marvellously made.

The Knowit

The Knowit is a tedious bird
  When you have homework waiting.
It knows the spelling of each word;
  It thrives on calculating.

It knows the boiling-point of glue;
  The cooling-point of lava;
It knows the dates of Good Queen Sue;
  The capital of Java . . .

Oh, certainly the Knowit is
  Spectacularly clever.
It must be, if it knows all this.
  But will it tell you? Never!

With hours of homework still to do
  (And slow and slow it's going)
It simply winks one eye at you
  And sits there, looking knowing.

More of Peter Dickinson's

IMPOSSIBLE PETS

Drawn by Raymond Briggs

The Fandango

By what may we tell the Fandango, my dears?
By his nondescript tail? His inadequate ears?
By his mouse-coloured fur? His forgettable beak?
No. What sets the Fandango apart is his

SHRIEK!!!!!

Do not take him along to an Arsenal match.
Do not play him a popular musical catch.
Keep him far from all Protests on Mass
                    Unemployment—
Or he'll let off his

SHRIEK!!!!!
          to display his enjoyment.

The Fandango's the world's most fanatical fan
And its noisiest (with the exception of Man).
His opinion is valueless, yet, nothing loth,
He will

SHRIEK!!!!!
          for the goodies, the baddies, or both.

Such vivacity may sound appealing, but yet
The Fandango is far from my favourite pet.

PROFESSOR Branestawm goes Cuckoo

κόκκυξ

NORMAN HUNTER

Mechanical noises took place outside Professor Branestawm's house, poppings occurred and two small clouds of smoke strolled past his window. But it wasn't an invention of the Professor's doing its thing a bit too burstingly. It was someone arriving.

Mrs Flittersnoop opened the door in her usual genteel manner, said 'Thank you very much I'm sure.' Then the noises broke out again, the clouds of smoke reversed past the window and the noises faded rapidly in the distance.

'From the Vicar, Sir,' said Mrs Flittersnoop coming into the Professor's study with a small but very nobbly parcel.

'Dear me,' said the Professor, looking at the parcel under and over various pairs of spectacles, 'I had no idea the Vicar went about in such an er excitable manner.'

'No sir, I'm sure sir,' said Mrs Flittersnoop. 'It wasn't the Vicar who brought it sir, it was the Misses Maisie and Daisy. In their cars sir,' she added, and then said 'good gracious me indeed sir,' as the Professor got the parcel undone.

A highly ornamental and very Black Forest looking clock fell out on the table. A determined little bird shot out of a trapdoor, said 'Cuckoo' three and half times and shot back again.

'A cuckoo clock!' cried Mrs Flittersnoop, 'how nice of the Vicar.'

'Tut, tut,' said the Professor. 'It is not at all nice of the Vicar. I really do not understand it. I er, that is to say um why doesn't he like it?'

'Like what sir?' asked Mrs Flittersnoop, guessing that something complicated was about to occur and guessing right.

'I sent this clock to the Vicar,' said the Professor, 'knowing that he favours, er traditional kinds of, ah things but apparently he has taken offence. He has sent it back without a word.'

The Vicar had done nothing of the kind. He had never seen the clock. Professor Branestawm had bought it at a little shop to send to the Vicar. But he'd written his own address on the label instead of the Vicar's because he was thinking of oval cogwheels. Then Maisie and Daisy, the Vicar's twin daughters happened to call at the shop later in their twin motor cars and the shopman asked them to deliver it at the Professor's as his delivery van was laid up with pains in the carburettor. But how was the Professor to know that; or Mrs Flittersnoop, or both of them together?

Just then the telephone rang.

'I hope you got the parcel safely,' said the Vicar's voice. 'My girls said they'd taken it over.'

Then there was a lot of highly assorted and mixed up explaining, by the end of which the Vicar had made it clear that there was nothing in this world he would like so much as a cuckoo clock, except perhaps a new organ for the church or a new church for the organ, according to which was the more dilapidated, and Professor Branestawm was under the impression that the Vicar didn't like the cuckoo clock under discussion but rather fancied having one invented by the Professor.

'Hm,' said the Professor, 'I suppose he wants a cuckoo clock that sings hymns at the quarter hours or reminds him when to say his sermon ... ha!' The Professor clapped a hand to his head and sent spectacles flying into orbit. 'What an idea! A cuckoo clock that instead of just saying "cuckoo" when the hour strikes, gives helpful reminders. Never been done before. I shall be the first person in the world to invent a genuine automatic reminding non-cuckoo clock. My name will go down to er er wherever it is names do go down to.'

The next minute he was off to his inventory. Mrs Flittersnoop hung the cuckoo clock carefully on the wall and wound it up, when it promptly said 'oo-cook' because something had gone backwards and Mrs Flittersnoop didn't know whether to take it as a compliment or as a slightly impertinent remark, coming from a wooden bird.

* * *

More mechanical noises were taking place, not outside the Professor's house but inside his inventory. And this time it definitely absolutely was an invention doing its thing.

'Bong bong bong bong,' came somewhat cracked chimes, then an even more cracked voice said 'Remember to choose the hymns for evening service.'

'Ha,' said the Professor gazing with some admiration at his newly invented non-cuckoo clock. It looked rather like a small cathedral with cinema influence. It had a throng of apprehensive angels round the bottom and a bent tower at the top. From this tower, through a highly gothic door, emerged a little bird in a cassock whenever the chimes rang out.

'Excellent,' murmured the Professor. He moved the hands of the clock round another hour. The chimes let go again and the cassocked cuckoo shot out and said, 'Pray remember to put your surplice out for the laundry, amen,' and shot in again.

'Very satisfying,' said the Professor. 'Now I must find out exactly what kind of things a vicar would want to be reminded about, then I can finish the clock and present it.'

But finding out what a vicar might want to be reminded about turned out to be a bit on the difficult side. Mrs Flittersnoop was all for having the clock arranged to remind him to change his underwear and not be late for dinner. The Dean of Great Pagwell considered the reminders should have to do with church matters such as matins and evensong and harvest festival. The verger wanted the reminder clock put over the pulpit to tell the congregation please to replace the prayer books before leaving, to save him having to do it. Doctor Mumpzanmeazle thought it presented an excellent opportunity for warning people of the dangers of infection in crowded buildings, in case the Vicar's church should ever get crowded. Colonel Dedshott thought the cuckoo shouldn't remind but should command and Commander Hardaport (Retired) thought it should give gale warnings and shipping forecasts. But

why the Vicar should need these wasn't clear as the only kind of wind that bothered him was the kind that was supposed to work the organ but frequently didn't.

All this expert advice didn't help the Professor much with the Vicar's non-cuckoo clock. But it gave him a severe rush of brains to the head and made him decide to make non-cuckoo reminder clocks for all his friends.

'They're very fond of saying I am er absent minded,' he said, taking a sip of ink in mistake for his morning coffee and wondering why it tasted cold. 'I shall show them that my mind is sufficiently present to remind them, er as it were, by remote control, of the things they should have remembered but may not have.'

* * *

To invent non-cuckoo reminding clocks for his friends was merely the work of goodness knows how long for the Professor. Then he invited them all to one of his celebrated demonstrations, while Mrs Flittersnoop, reinforced by Sister Aggie and a few friends prepared suitable refreshments for coping with the situation, let's hope.

But by the time Colonel Dedshott, the Vicar, the Mayor, Commander Hardaport (Retired) and everybody else the Professor had invited were compressed into the Professor's dining room, along with the clocks, which took up nearly as much space as they did, nobody had any room to eat and only just enough room to speak.

'This one is for the Mayor,' said the Professor, starting up a noticeably municipal-looking clock with the arms of Great Pagwell on the front and 'No Parking' notices on each side.

'Ding dong. Remember to declare open M592 motorway between Great Pagwell and Pagwell Green,' croaked a little bird in a cocked hat.

'Hrrrrm,' said the Mayor who didn't agree much with motorways since one had only just missed his dining room.

'And here is one for Commander Hardaport,' said the Professor, permitting to get under way a clock with several funnels, and one or two masts. It had weights shaped like anchors.

'Dong-dong dong-dong dong-dong dong-dong.' The clock very properly rang up eight bells, which made it a reasonable sort of tea time and a small seagull in a naval cap with a telescope under its wing shouted very crisply 'Belay there weed the starboard flower bed.'

'Aye, aye,' cried the Commander, trying to salute but finding the Vicar and Doctor Mumpzanmeazle too much in the way.

'Now for the Doctor's clock,' continued the Professor.

An extremely medical clock with red crosses on its sides and smelling strongly of antiseptic went 'Ding ding ding ding' like a fairly frantic ambulance. Then out shot a little bird in nurse's uniform and snapped 'Time for a spot check on spotty patients in surgery, please doctor.' Brandished a thermometer and shot in again.

Colonel Dedshott's clock resembled a high class military tent, emitted a bugle call instead of a chime and a little sergeant bird clicked himself to attention and roared out 'By the left, change socks,' clicked again and vanished.

'My word by jove what!' exclaimed the Colonel.

Other non-cuckoo reminding clocks for the Vicar, Lord Pagwell of the Pagwell Publishing Company, the Headmaster of Pagwell College and other dignified friends of the Professor all performed suitably. Then Mrs Flittersnoop popped out of the kitchen like a rather large cuckoo and announced refreshments, which had to be taken in the front garden as there was no eating room anywhere else and none too much even there.

'Remarkable invention of the Pro-fessors I must say,' said the Mayor, feeling a bit downcast at not being able to declare anything open.

'Oh very, I mean to say yus, cor-blimey what a lark not arf I don't fink,' said a road-sweeping friend of sister Aggie's who'd come to help with the washing up.

Then, when everyone had had as much to eat as they wanted, or as much as they could get at before someone else got it, the party broke up. The Professor's friends went home carrying their special clocks. Mrs Flittersnoop and friends tackled the washing up and the spare refresh-ments they'd had the foresight to hide away for later use. And the Pro-fessor went happily off to give a lec-ture he wasn't due to give until next Tuesday.

continued on page 60

WILL NOBODY PAT MY HICCUP?

A reminder of a real-life absent-minded professor

Funny and eccentric as he seems to us when we read about him, Norman Hunter's marvellous Professor Branestawm would probably seem fairly normal among a crowd of real-life professors, even with the five pairs of spectacles perched on his forehead. For, especially as they get older, a lot of clever people develop a sort of learned dottiness. Probably because with weighty things on their minds they cannot be bothered with minor every day affairs.

The most famous of real-life absent-minded professors was the beloved and delightful Dr Spooner, who was warden of New College, Oxford at the beginning of the century. Nowadays his eccentricities are recorded in the Oxford Dictionary . . . where they define a 'spoonerism' as '*an accidental transposition of initial sounds or other parts of two or more words*'.

His reputation probably started when he announced a hymn in the Chapel College as *Kinkering Kongs their Tatles Tike*. One of his students reported being told '*you have deliberately tasted two worms and can leave Oxford by the town drain*'.

After that the wits of Oxford went to work and before long they declared that the good Doctor had preached from his pulpit, '*we all, I believe, have a half-warmed fish in our hearts*,' that he had declared that the most memorable sight in Egypt was *the minx by spoonlight*, had reproached somebody in chapel for *occupewing my pie*, and during a high wind was seen chasing his hat down the pavement calling '*please, will nobody pat my hiccup?*'

But perhaps the favourite story about him is his dramatic account of the cat who fell out of a window in the warden's lodgings, which ended:- '*But no matter, she popped on her drawers and away she went*'.

One wizzy Wednesday later on, Colonel Dedshott had his breakfast interrupted by the sergeant bird from his clock, who shot out, sprang to attention and bellowed 'Fall in to choose hymns for evening service.'

The same afternoon Doctor Mumpzanmeazle's clock rang its ambulance bell and the nurse bird cried 'Foundation stone for the new primary school to be laid three times a day after meals.'

The Doctor fired a heavy pill at it and went out, colliding with Commander Hardaport who was steaming past his gate.

'Ha Doctor!' cried the Commander. 'Funny thing happened this morning. That confounded clock Professor Branestawm made for me started reminding me to give anti-flu injections to the lifeboats. Said my port engine was suffering from rheumatism. How'd it get itself mixed up with your clock, hey?'

The Doctor was just about to tell him about his clock when the Vicar came rumbling past on his bicycle, carrying his non-cuckoo clock which was singing out to the tune of 'Onward Christian Soldiers' 'Don't forget to scrub the decks; swab the scuppers out.' He was followed closely by the Mayor, Lord Pagwell and the Chief of the Fire Brigade, each clutching a clock that was emitting highly unsuitable instructions, reminders and commands.

'This is most irregular,' declared the Mayor. 'We must return these contraptions to the Professor at once. I am afraid they may utter some instructions that will be contrary to the bye laws.'

Doctor Mumpzanmeazle dashed into his house and came out with his clock, still uttering mixed municipal and medical prescriptions.

Illustrations and cartoon by
GEORGE ADAMSON

'To the Professor's,' he cried 'most urgent. We don't want to let this develop into an epidemic.'

They all shot off, collected Colonel Dedshott and the Vicar and surged round to Professor Branestawm's house with all the clocks telling them what to do and when to do it.

'Ah yes,' said the Professor when he'd managed to get the clocks to stop shouting and Colonel Dedshott and the rest to stop talking. 'I rather fear it was an um er mistake to bring the clocks together for my demonstration. The juxtaposition of their electronic mechanisms has possibly caused some unwise integration of the radio active waves between them.'

'Sounds like mutiny to me,' cried Commander Hardaport 'Clap 'em in irons I say.'

'Vast heaving,' cried the Commander's clock.

'Stop talking in the ranks there,' shouted the Colonel's clock.

'Change your vest three times a day before giving a sermon on bad drains,' retorted the Doctor's clock getting more mixed up than ever.

'Who are you calling a drain,' bellowed Lord Pagwell's clock to the Doctor's.

'Shut up,' retorted the Doctor's clock.

Then the most unreasonable arguments broke out among the clocks. They called one another rude names of the most unheard of kinds. They commanded one another to get knotted, drop dead, and jump in plenty of lakes.

'As you were,' shouted Colonel Dedshott, sounding like his own non-cuckoo clock sergeant bird only louder. He hit the clock with a poker. It collapsed in the middle and the bird sergeant squawked 'Turn out the guard, who goes there with foundation stones and hymn books.'

Then the other clocks started throwing their weights about. The Commander's clock hooked the

Mayor's clock with one of his anchor shaped weights and pulled two No Parking notices off it. The Mayor's clock retaliated with a direct hit on the Vicar's angels. The Commander's clock joined up with the Doctor's clock and laid into the Colonel's clock which started reading out the ten commandments.

Bash, wallop, dong dong 'Remember to change your socks on the motorway,' Ding a ling ding 'Distribute the starboard hymn books' Bong crash rattle bim 'Who's a wooden faced indigestion pill?' Bang crash 'Shut up.' 'Lie down.' Wallop 'Oh come all ye faithful' Crash. 'Pass friend and drop dead.' Bong.

Colonel Dedshott and Commander Hardaport grabbed a handful of fire irons but before they could attack with them, the fighting clocks swung their weights at them, wound their chains rounds the pokers and things and snatched them away.

'Take them in the rear, Commander,' bellowed Colonel Dedshott 'I'll attack from the flank.'

Commander Hardaport leapt out of the window and was instantly arrested by two policemen looking for promotion.

'Now then,' they said 'what's all this then?'

The answer came as the clocks threw the Mayor out of the window.

'Help,' shrieked Mrs. Flittersnoop.

'Guards, change your starboard socks,' yelled the clocks.

'Rescue!' bellowed Colonel Dedshott attacking with a best dining room chair.

'The patient's temperature is hymn two hundred and three,' roared the clocks, pushing the Colonel and the chair through the french doors.

Chaos and confusion reigned, in fact they poured. Colonel Dedshott snatched a policeman's walkie talkie and tried to call up the Catapult Cavaliers. But before the police station he got onto could sort things out the pandemonium in the Professor's house died down as the clocks finally demolished one another and with a last faint cry of 'Remember to open the Motor Way Bazaar in aid of Chinese orphans' the battle ceased. Then with the help of the Fifth Upper Pagwell Troup of Scouts, who happened to be passing on their way to or from somewhere, The Professor's house was tidied up and the bits of demolished clocks safely stowed in the most distant municipal rubbish dump.

'Do you dig cuckoo clocks?' said Maisie to Daisy, as they arrived just too late to take the Vicar home as he had already got away in a police van, along the Commander Hardaport, the Mayor and Lord Pagwell.

'Strictly for the birds,' said Daisy to Maisie or vice versa. And they disappeared down the road in two identical clouds of noisy smoke.

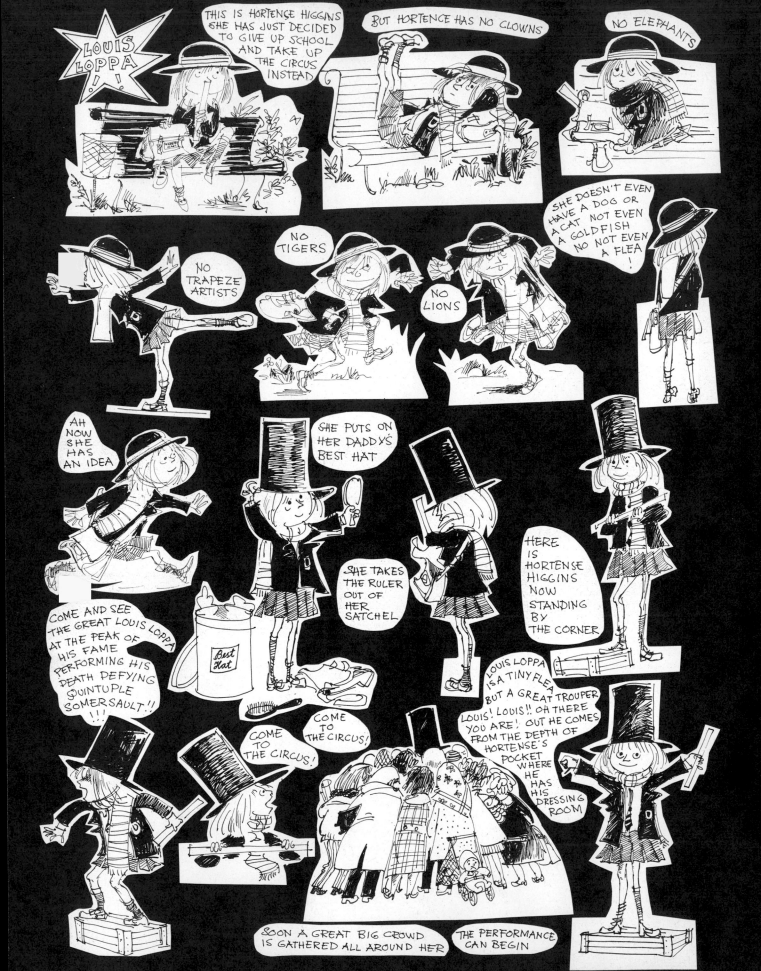

in pictures by Gunvor Edwards

Captain Pugwash Rides The Waves

John Ryan, creator of Captain Pugwash and Sir Prancelot tells us how his stories are made into films for the television screen.

If you think that I make cartoon programmes in the same way as Walt Disney cartoons, you're wrong. These kind of films are made by what is known as 'stop-frame' animation, and are very expensive and take a long time and a lot of people. The illusion of movement is given by showing twenty-five different pictures every second and very large numbers of artists and technicians are involved. My method is far simpler. Most of the work is done by three of us in my studio; and, although in terms of movement the result may be less convincing, it is a much cheaper and quicker way of telling stories on the television screen, and it seems to work.

This is how we do it: To begin with, each Pugwash film has to have a story outline, known as the 'script'; and, of course, before I write the story I have to have an idea. Sometimes I wake up with one, sometimes I sit for hours thinking. And sometimes I just draw a scene –

a wild tropical jungle for example – and then try to imagine what might happen to my characters in such a place. I first invented Captain Pugwash over twenty years ago, so by now I usually find it easy to work out how he and his friends and enemies will behave in different situations.

Once the script is written, we start making the pictures. We call these 'captions'. We need about fifty of them for a five-minute film. First we make the characters like flat puppets. They are cut out of card and laid on painted backgrounds. Then they are moved by cardboard levers and the whole caption is put together with tiny brass paperclips and glue and sticky paper. We use different coloured card and paper to save having to paint everything. I do most of the drawing, Sara Cole adds colour to the figures and backgrounds, and Hazel Martingell cuts them out, puts them together and makes them work. We have to work fast; it takes us about a fortnight to make the captions for one film.

Almost as important as the pictures is the sound. At the recording studio we meet Peter Hawkins, the actor whose ability to speak with any number of different voices is truly amazing.

Peter tells the story and speaks the parts of all the characters into the microphone, and it's very hard to keep a straight face as he does it because he has a way of miming the action as well! Then we make the sound effects, clashing table knives for a sword fight, for example, and choose other noises, such as explosions, from the record library. The music is specially composed and played by Johnny Pearson for the Pugwash series. Finally my editor Barry Shephard mixes voices, sound effects and music onto a 16 millimetre magnetic sound track. And he times it, so that it lasts exactly five minutes.

When we have completed the sound track and the captions (incidentally fifty of them mounted on thick card make quite a heavy load) we set off for a small film studio in North London which specialises in puppet animation. It is an exciting house filled with miniature

continued on page 67

The Black Pig in port

Quayside: Captain Pugwash boards his ship

The Captain's breakfast, Tom in attendance

The Mate, anxious

Pirates in conference

Cannon practice

Preparing for action

Cut-throat Jake comes ashore

Treasure!

"Help! It's Cut-throat Jake!"

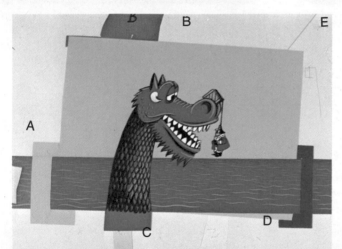

Above left: Jake and his crew with a fit of the sneezes. Above: Pugwash and Tom in the dinghy

Left: Pugwash and the Sea-monster. This shows how the levers operate:
'A' pulls the sea through to give forward movement. 'B' opens the monster's eye, 'C' the monster's mouth, 'D' shudders Pugwash and 'E' moves the whole caption up and down to give extra movement.

The pirates have a party.

Clap your hands and sing . . .

film sets and puppets of every description. Usually the experts, Bob Burn and John Hardwick, produce 'stop-frame' animation but for Pugwash they provide lighting and a 16 millimetre camera so that we can film our pictures at work just as actors are filmed in the making of a full-scale film.

The illustration below was actually taken with different helpers because we were making the 'Sir Prancelot' series, but it shows how the captions are set up, with all of us gathered round the easel.

photo: Birra and Hardwick

Each of us has a job to do in the animation of the picture. Priscilla, my wife, usually looks after the levers which control the mouth movements. Hazel operates the tape recorder and keeps a careful log of the filming. Thus if the first picture shows Captain Pugwash saying '*Full speed ahead, me hearties*' we listen to the tape several times while Priscilla practices the mouth movements, Sara works the Captain's eyes and I look after the arms and make them point in the right direction at the right time. When we all know what to do we film that little bit of the story.

If something goes wrong the first time we shoot it again.

We go right through the whole story, filming each scene in order and keeping a careful note of what has happened. At the end of the day we have probably used up about 400 feet of film and have the whole story 'in the can'. This goes off to the laboratory to be processed and comes back two days later in the form of a colour negative (which is precious and must not be touched), and rough prints in black and white which are known as 'rushes'.

We look at these on a screen to see if anything has gone wrong, and we retake anything that has. For example, we have to make sure that the camera has only taken the picture itself and hasn't 'shot off' to reveal the levers and even the hands of the people working them. In the colour illustrations on the previous pages you can see the difference between the picture as you will see it on your TV screen and the whole caption with the working parts round the edge. You will notice too that some pictures are different shapes, some long and some larger than others. This is so that John Hardwick our cameraman can zoom in and out on some scenes or move about over the picture if needed.

The final stage is the editing and this takes me back to Barry (who helped to make the sound-track in the first place). He has a special machine which enables us to play the sound on the one side and see the picture on a miniature screen on the other. 'Edit-

ing' means choosing the best film sequences, and cutting them into lengths so that they fit exactly to the sound-track. When all the bits have been joined together we have what is known as a 'rough-cut' film, in black and white which is good enough to examine and decide on any changes which might be necessary. And when the film is finally approved in this form, the negative is cut and joined to match it and the laboratories produce the colour print. And this is the film which, with the sound track, goes to the BBC and will eventually be transmitted onto your television screen.

All of this may sound like a very long operation just to produce one five-minute film, but in fact it is far quicker than other methods of animation. Even so, it will take us about ninety weeks to make the whole series of thirty, five-minute stories. As I am writing this I have completed fourteen of my new series. I haven't the faintest idea what the next sixteen adventures will be about, but with luck and a certain amount of hard thinking the ideas will come. Then they will be shown on television.

We start off with nothing more than a few sheets of coloured card, watercolour paints, glue and brass paper-clips. Three weeks later, with the help of all the skilful people I have mentioned, we have a film. It's all a lot of fun, and if I can entertain you all and at the same time make a living out of it I'm very happy.

HERE BE DRAGONS . . .

BRUCE CARTER visits the remote Pacific islands of the Galapagos and finds rare and fabulous creatures living peacefully out of reach of mankind . . .

We managed to struggle safely ashore on to the black lava rock. It was a bad place to slip. Offshore there were sting-rays (twenty feet across!) and sharks. Not good for swimming. These rocks weren't very friendly either. They were jagged and so hot to the touch you could have fried gulls' eggs on them. Out of the fire and into the frying pan? Yes—we soon were thinking.

If you are going back in time a million or more years, you don't necessarily expect a warm welcome. Or familiar, friendly natives. What we saw now were black, very large sea lions. Except for their size they looked like the sea lions one can see today in most zoos. They were lying uncomfortably on the rocks, a few yards from us. Sometimes their grunts turned to coughs, as if they had smoked fifty cigarettes a day all their lives.

Farther along the shore a great bull sea lion with a domed head was keeping guard over his twenty-five wives and pups. His dark glistening body, scarred by many a fight, rocked threateningly from side to side.

Because of their protective colouring we didn't spot the dragons for several minutes.

When we saw the first one, only a few yards away, our hearts leapt half in disbelief, half in fear. It couldn't really be a dragon, of course. Yet what else? Its head had the texture of the lava rock on which it lay, staring unblinkingly at us. Its mouth, forever in a mirthless grin, was like the slit of a letter-box. Sharp spines ran the length of its back, and all along its powerful tail. Its plump scaley body was like a badly stuffed toy animal, with bulges and creases that came and went when it moved. It walked on four pudgy legs, each with five sharp-pointed fingers like a knight's gauntlets. It was four feet long, which is short for a dragon but big for a lizard.

When we bent down it suddenly shot out a stream of liquid at us from its nostrils. It might have been a dragon's fire.

This was in fact a marine iguana. And it is harmless to man. Just as well, too, because when we looked about that black lava beach more closely we saw dozens more, all lying in the mid-day vertical sun, some youngsters, some fully grown, waiting for the tide to go down. When it was low enough to expose the seaweed, they would lumber off and graze on it. It was their only food. Not at all like St George's dragon.

Black rock, black sea lions, black herons, black iguana. When we began to walk inland, dark lizards

A MARINE IGUANA . . . *"it suddenly shot out a stream of liquid from its nostrils . . . it might have been dragon's fire"*

by the score scuttled from under our feet. When we looked up, the blackest of black birds floated lazily about the sky, like archaeopteryx. They were Frigate, or Man-o'-War birds, with a 7½-foot wingspan. Effortless in flight, and as nimble and manoeuvrable as a bumble bee.

Frigates are like primeval pirates of the sky. If they spot (and they have eyes like radio telescopes) a bird with a fish in its beak, they will follow it as it twists and turns, harassing and pecking at it in mid-flight until it releases its catch. Then they will drop like a stone, catch the fish before it strikes the sea—and gobble it up.

There are too many frigates in the sky to count, from thirty to three thousand feet high. We're going to try to find their nests.

Feeling more than ever as if time has stood still on this strange island, we leave behind the black lava rock shore, and force our way inland. The sun is so lethal it burns through our hats and our long-sleeve shirts. We are slap on the equator. Every morning the deep red, twice-as-large-as-life sun heaves itself out of the sea at exactly 6.20 am. All day it fries and roasts and boils everything it touches. At 6.20 pm it hits the sea (with a hiss?) and is gone. It has been like that since the beginning of time, for here there are no seasons.

We push through the salt bushes and *opuntia* cactus trees. Cheeky brown mocking birds follow us. They are about the size of an English thrush but not so tidily dressed—rough but friendly. If we stand still they perch on our shoes and look up quizzically. 'What do you want?' we ask. Action speaks louder than words. This one flutters up onto the blond head of the young naturalist who is accompanying us on this trek. The bird takes out half a dozen hairs. 'That'll add a bit of colour to his nest,' says our naturalist, rubbing the sore place.

Nothing is afraid of us. We almost trip over a Bluefoot Booby on its nest—if you call a few sticks and stones on the ground a nest. It is six weeks old and sits up straight, eyeing us craftily, and it clucks its beak if we go right up to it. Its mother lands with a whoosh of wings. She's as big as a fat goose, and her beak as well as her big webbed feet are as bright blue as the sky from which she has dropped. The chick opens wide its fat greedy beak, and mother puts her own beak down its throat and releases its dinner.

After a long hot struggle

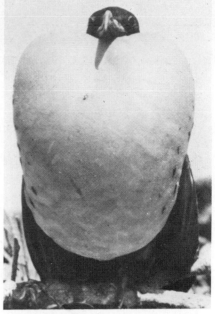

THE MALE MAGNIFICENT FRIGATEBIRD . . . *"inflates his scarlet throat in a mating display"*

through the thorny undergrowth we found the first frigate nests—built on the top of shrubs—rotten nests they were, too, just a layer of uncomfortable-looking twigs. Frigates build as high as they can because they are so enormous and have such big wings that they have difficulty in taking off from the ground.

When we came near, the adults, patrolling high above like night bombers of the First World War, came lower as if to protect their young.

THE BLUE FOOTED BOOBY AND CHICKS . . . *"its nest a few sticks and stones on the bare ground"*

Like the ticks, we were finally driven out by the sun. On the way back to the sea we lay in the shade for a few minutes. Suddenly through the grass we saw a fearsome face staring at us. It was a land iguana, even bigger than the marine ones we had seen earlier—its long dragon-like body and twitching tail blending in perfectly with its surroundings. We offered it yellow cactus flowers and its great teeth tore them to shreds with relish. 'They like the same food as the tortoises,' our naturalist told us. We had seen these tortoises earlier —giant ones weighing a quarter of a ton, and we had even ridden on them. They didn't mind. The tortoises (Galapagos in Spanish) are the biggest, most memorable things you see on the islands. Huge, slow-moving, cumbersome, they come in eleven different subspecies, some with saddle-shaped shells and long necks where the vegetation is high and hard to reach. Poor tortoises! They've had a rough time in the past. Before the days of refrigeration and conservation, sailors used to collect them by the hundred and throw them in the holds of their ships. They live up to a year without food or water, so the sailors had turtle soup and meat, whenever they wanted it.

* * * * *

We were on North Seymour, one of the Galapagos Islands that lie across the equator six hundred miles off Ecuador in South America. They are exciting and unique. Even expert scientists don't completely understand these islands. They are volcanic. That is clear enough from the tens of thousands of craters, some a few yards across, some many miles wide and 5,000 feet high.

The real mystery begins with the fauna. Nowhere else in the world can you find marine iguanas, cormorants that cannot fly, and no fewer than thirteen different subspecies of giant tortoises. Even the four different sorts of mockingbirds are endemic —or unique—to these islands. Then the Galapagos Islands have their own special albatross and their own fur seal and penguin—all of which you can find only in the Antarctic or sub-Antarctic.

Scientists believe that they came north hundreds of thousands of years ago with the cold current that runs from the Antarctic, up the coasts of Chile, Peru and Ecuador and then swings west at the equator to these islands. They can live here only because the water is cool. They have adapted themselves as best they can to the heat of the sun.

These sixty-one islands and islets were thrown up from the seabed of the Pacific Ocean between three and one million years ago by volcanic eruption. Some of the islands are still volcanically eruptive today—especially on the western island of Narborough.

Their origin is clear enough. But how they came to be inhabited by such primeval and unique fauna is less certain. Most scientists today believe that this same current brought with it fragments of flooded river banks, old tree trunks and other river flotsam. These provided rafts for some very frightened passengers—iguanas, lizards, insects, perhaps giant tortoises and turtle eggs.

If this is what happened,

REDBILLED TROPICAL BIRD . . . *"basks on a rock surrounded by iguanas"*

it happened before predatory mammals stalked the world, destroying for food or just for fun these defenceless giant tortoises and iguanas. And of all these mammals, none was more destructive than *homo sapiens*—cruel man! But these nasty mammals did not reach the Galapagos (or not until recently), and that is why, for instance, marine iguanas still live on these beaches today, reminding us of fabulous dragons and pre-history.

The first naturalist to land on these islands was Charles Darwin in 1835. Amongst all the other wonders, his keen scientific eyes observed that the fauna had adapted to its environment. From what he learned on these islands, Darwin many years later wrote the most famous and revolutionary book of natural history—*The Origin of Species*. In 1959, one hundred years after it was published, a laboratory was set up on one of the Galapagos islands to help the study of the unique wild life, and to help preserve these bewitched or enchanted islands—the *islas encantadas* as the Spaniards called them.

* * *

We clambered back into our dinghy. A pair of brown pelicans had joined the black sea lions, the black lava herons, the black iguanas, on the shore. They stretched their great wings as we left, and lifted off, only to plunge seconds later into the surf, shopping-basket-beak first —splash! One came up with a tasty fish. You could follow its progress down the bird's long neck . . .

AS YET UNHARMED BY MAN . . . *Creatures of the Galapagos basking in the tropical sun. 1. Marine Iguana at rest. 2. Land Iguana at lunch. 3. Bull Seal in full cry. 4. The Fabulous Giant Tortoise (from which the Galapagos takes its name) weighing a quarter of a ton.*

AMAZING ACHIEVEMENTS

of Days Gone By

Gems from the Improbable Puffin Book of Records invented and illustrated by QUENTIN BLAKE

The astonishing record for the Croydon to Macclesfield Long Distance Leapfrog Race – three days four and a half hours – was set up in 1867 by the Clerkenwell Solicitors' First Team and remains unbroken to this day.

Gaspard's Leap. A legendary moment in the history of Snail Racing. In the Overland Obstacle race of 1894 a French racing snail called Gaspard le Terrible took the lead at a critical moment with an amazing leap of over 1½ inches!

The Lydia Gripe Award for the Nastiest School Dinner of the Century was awarded in 1899 to St Simeon's Academy for a plate of something unidentifiable.

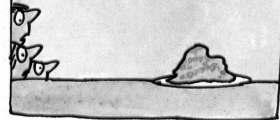

Hairiest Dog. At the Grand International Congress of Hairiness in 1882 the prize in the canine division was awarded to Grand Smudger of Salisbury. On the left are two of the runners-up.

The longest scarf ever knitted by an 89-year-old grandmother in the county of Rutland on a Wednesday was recorded in 1853. It was 37 yards long.

World's Laziest Duck. A duck called Simpson in Compton Martin in Somerset lay on its back from May 1st to October 24th 1891.

In an incredible feat of endurance Elsie Grommett travelled from Land's End to John o'Groats on her Lightfoot's Clockwork Roller Skates. It took her five months, two weeks, and three and a half hours.

The largest number of penguins ever recorded in a telephone box at one time was in Old Brompton Road in London in 1904. There were 149 of them, together with an old lady who was trying to make a telephone call.

At the Jugglers' Convention of 1923 Mr. H. A. Noop, an encyclopedia salesman, won the Christmas Pudding Juggling Finals by keeping nine puddings in the air for 3¾ hours. Unfortunately on this occasion one of the puddings caught in the rafters of the Penge Horticultural Hall, where the event was taking place, and the building was burnt to the ground.

73

How to make a Puffin Kite

Man first felt the thrill of a kite pulling and soaring in the sky above him as long ago as 2000 BC, and the first references we can find to making kites appear in early Chinese legends. One of these is about a Chinese emperor who was at his wits' end to know how to drive an invading army from his beleaguered palace walls, so he went up to the ramparts to survey his plight. Now the wise man he took with him wore a flat hat and, as they stood looking, the wind suddenly whipped the hat off his head and it rose into the sky and floated towards the enemy. This gave them the idea of making a number of flat kites to which they fitted sounding devices made from bamboo, rather like organ pipes. When night came the kites drifted over the enemy below, who, on hearing the weird wailing as the wind rushed through the pipes, thought the gods were angry with them and fled in panic.

The Chinese also used kites as signals, rather as we used bonfires in the early days; they would send one up into the sky to warn their friends if an enemy was approaching.

In Korea and the islands in that part of the world kites were used for fishing. Hooks were suspended from the kites; then they were flown out to sea so that the fisherman could make his catch in deeper waters.

On these pages CONRAD BAILEY, champion kite designer, has shown you how to make a kite shaped like a puffin. It won't catch fish for you, or disperse a hostile army, but it will flap its wings and, we hope, give you a lot of pleasure.

MAKING A PUFFIN KITE

Always remember when making any kite that the lighter the materials, the better it will fly. If you balance it correctly it will not need too much adjustment when completed. Follow the directions carefully and you will have a strong high-flying kite.

Choosing Your Materials

The following list is the most suitable and most of the materials can be found quite easily, but, if some are not obtainable, substitutes can be used — i.e., strong light sticks can be used for the body of Puffin: Polythene, in place of light Japanese paper though it is difficult to paint on.

STICKS. Five thin canes, one at least 40 in. long, $\frac{3}{32}$ in. in diameter. This is used in other crafts (see list of suppliers). One thicker cane ($\frac{3}{16}$ in. garden cane). This can be carefully split. Always pierce and split cane from middle, not from top. You will find it is easier and more accurate.

KITE SURFACE. Thin Japanese paper or rice paper. These are light and the surface is good for painting on. Size at least 40 in. x 14 in. If paper is smaller than 40 in. long join two sheets together with glue.

THIN THREAD. For binding cane.

GLUE. Quick drying type is best. I have found Super Epoxy the finest, but as this involves mixing, Uhu is the most convenient.

SCISSORS, KNIFE, PAINTS. For decorating kite.

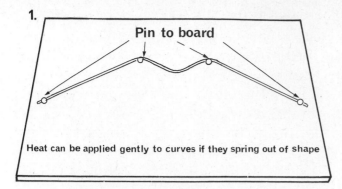

1.

Pin to board

Heat can be applied gently to curves if they spring out of shape

STEP 1 Take the 40 in. length of cane and place it in a bath of water so that it is completely covered and leave for at least two hours. This will make the cane supple. Then place on a wood board or surface as in diagram. This will take some time to dry meanwhile—

STEP 2 Take the thicker cane (split garden cane). This should be 18 in. long. To check for balance find the centre at 9 in., put it on your finger with the mark in middle of finger. If it weighs *down* at one end, shave off a little of the cane at this end until it balances exactly.

STEP 3 Cut two pieces 4 in. long off one of the thin canes and mark the middle of each. Place one piece 2 in. from end of thick cane. Bind and glue to form cross. This will be the head end of Puffin. Do the same at other end but place 4 in. from end of centre cane. This will be the tail.

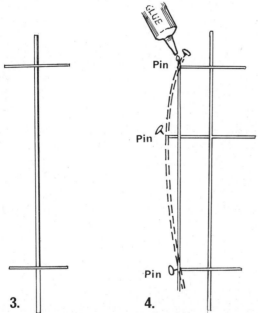

3.   **4.**

STEP 4 Cut two pieces of thin cane 18 in. long. Lay one piece on top of cross pieces with a slight overlap at the top cross (see diagram.) Put small amount of glue on each surface. Lay on board and insert drawing pin near joint to hold until dry. When dry, bind with thin thread, and this can have a little glue on it when the other end is glued. Before binding and gluing bottom joint, bow out the cane. This can be done easily by pinning on board. Make the widest point 3 in. Repeat the instructions on other side. Fix middle cross piece into position 6 in. from top cross only binding and gluing sides. *Do not glue and bind to centre stick.*

STEP 5 Find a very pliable piece of the thin cane and bind and glue across the two sides, bowing it in a nice curve to form Puffin's head. To form tail, warm up the point where bottom cross is formed, bend gently outwards, repeat on other side.

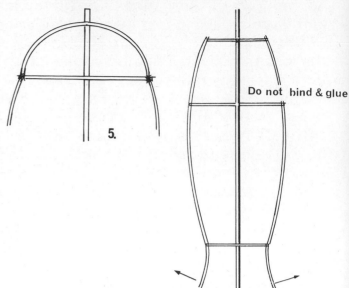

5.

Do not bind & glue

Heat gently and bend

STEP 6 The body of bird can now be covered. Cut a rectangle of paper big enough to allow a ½ in. overlap all round. Draw shape plus overlap in pencil, cut out with scissors. Now CHECK FOR BALANCE. Hold frame at the tail-end of middle cane. Place top of head on table edge. If it is balanced on finger it should not heel over to left or right. If it does go over on its side a thin piece of cane should be sello-taped on the light side until the frame stays still on finger.

Cover the frame with shaped paper turning paper over at edges and gluing. Where it is curved cut notches in paper and glue, see diagram.

STEP 7 If the wing cane has dried and retained its shape it can be slipped under centre cane, and making sure you have found and marked centre point of wing-cane, bind and glue onto body.

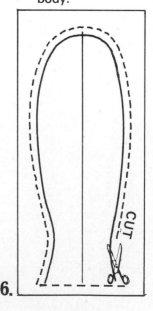

6.   CUT

Turn over and glue

STEP 8 Place construction on your large rectangle of Japanese paper (40 in. x 14 in.). Draw round shape of wings looking at squared drawing of Puffin for shape of wing. Note ½ in. overlap at front of wings. Cut out shape with scissors.

Put wings on board and dampen most of the surface of wings except front portion (a sponge is best for this purpose). Wrinkle up the damp paper, do not make any tears. When dry smooth out carefully. This will give a rough texture to the wings.

STEP 9 Put body and wing assembly on paper wing cut-out, leaving at least ½ in. on leading edge for turning over. Cut notches on curves as for body, and glue, turning over cane, slip the wings under centre cane.

N.B. Heat can be applied to cane by using a candle flame with care.

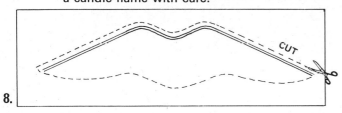
8.

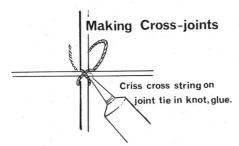

Making Cross-joints

Criss cross string on joint tie in knot, glue.

Drawing and Painting the Puffin

Using the pattern drawn on graph paper you can make a copy by enlarging the squares to the size of your kite and copy detail on your kite. Paint with quick-drying felt pens or brushes and inks.

Making the Beak

Cut a rectangle of fairly stiff cartridge paper 6 in. x 3 in. Fold it in half and draw beak colouring as drawing. Glue the inside surface, cut out shape, leaving ½ in. to bend at right angles. Sellotape it on each flap onto Puffin's face.

FOLD

Stick with tape

Making a Bridle

The bridle controls the angle at which the surface meets the wind.

The wind or air will lift the kite by being diverted downward along the face of the kite upwards.

Turn kite onto its back. Make a hole each side of head as diagram.

Thread string 9 in. long through each hole and tie with strong knot.

Make two holes at tail-end, thread 12 in. of string through holes and tie this to centre stick.

Take curtain ring and tie all three strings through ring. A single knot will suffice. Seal this single knot with a piece of adhesive tape. When the correct position has been found strings can be tied with a double knot.

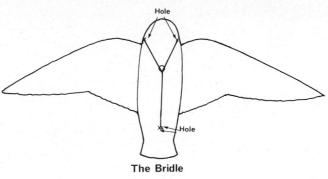

Hole

Hole

The Bridle

Making the Tail

This can be a 3 in. wide strip of thin polythene attached to end of centre stick or an alternative tail is made by attaching 4 in. strips of light paper at 8 in. intervals along a piece of string (see diagram.)

NUFFIN LIKE A PUFFIN

Flying Your Kite

Choose an open space. Buildings and trees get in the way and break the wind up.

Stand with your back to the wind. Hold kite by the towing ring. The wind will lift it into the air, it should not be necessary to run with the kite.

Try not to throw kite into the air.

As it rises let line out slowly until it is well into the air. Help it by pulling gently on line. This is done by holding line at arms' length. Bend your arms up and back at elbow. As you straighten arm up slowly let line slip through fingers. Do this until kite is high in the sky. If you have carried out the instructions your Puffin should fly well. If you still have difficulty try readjusting the bridle or altering the length of tail.

Four Rules for Adjusting Bridle or Tail

1 If it won't rise it may be flying too vertically. Move towing ring nearer top of bridle.

2. If it flutters or dips it is probably flying too flat. Move towing ring nearer middle of bridle.

3 If your kite spins or dives or does a loop, add a longer or heavier tail.

4 If kite does not rise and tail hangs down, shorten tail.

A Few Hints

Do not fly your kite near trees, high tension cables, telephone wires or airfields.

Do not fly a kite with a wet line. It will cut your hands.

Do not fly your kite above 200 ft. This is the maximum the law permits.

Yet another of Peter Dickinson's
IMPOSSIBLE PETS
Drawn by Raymond Briggs

The Scapedog

The Scapedog is a beast of sin,
  A villain of the deepest dye.
But if you chance to spot one in
  A pet-shop, grab your purse and buy!
He'll wreck your house, but do not fuss.
He's wicked for the rest of us.

He'll steal your supper, gnaw your hats,
  Bark like a fiend at three a.m.
He'll chase the postman. As for cats,
  He'll put the fear of God in them.
But all your family (behold!)
Will suddenly be good as gold.

I knew a charming family–
  So sweet, so kind, so pure–who had
A Scapedog for a pet, and he
  Was extra-double-record bad.
They felt too good for such a scamp
And gave him to a passing tramp.

Next day that sweet and charming mother
  Wrote three rude letters to the Pope.
Papa held up some bank or other.
  The children found a piece of rope
And rustled Farmer Helmore's cow . . .

The tramp's become a bishop now.

AUTHORS AND PLACES

We have been asking our Puffin authors to show us some of the real life places which they have used in their books. Sometimes it is just the *kind of scenery* which starts their inspiration flowing; sometimes it's simply the room they prefer writing in; and sometimes they have taken us to the very spot on which one of their characters had an adventure. But in every case it has given us a chance to show you what they look like. There are more on page 95, but if we've left out someone that you particularly want to know about please tell us, and we'll put them in Puffin Annual No. 2.

Leon Garfield

When I was young, in the dark days of November, my way home from school lay through the graveyard of St Nicholas's church in Brighton. With shadows beckoning, it was a gloomy spot, and the iron railings round the grand tombs seemed more to keep the dead inside than such as me from trespassing. I seem to remember it was always busy with ghastly nuns and hanged monks . . . so much so that I persuaded my good friends, Bostock and Harris, always to accompany me. In mortal terror, we crept through . . . then hid among headstones till the girls from the High School came giggling by (how insensitive they were!) when we leapt out at them with hideous shrieks and groans and sights unholy! In those far-off days, we only longed to frighten girls.

Born in Brighton.
Lives in London.

Books in Puffin:
MISTER CORBETT'S GHOST
BLACKJACK
DEVIL-IN-THE-FOG
JACK HOLBORN
SMITH
THE DRUMMER BOY
THE STRANGE AFFAIR OF ADELAIDE HARRIS

Norman Hunter

I don't live in Great Pagwell, I live near Staines on the Thames, where they used to make linoleum and where I now make Professor Branestawm stories. It's very convenient really, because behind the fireplace in my study, which you can see in the picture, there is a secret passage leading to Professor Branestawm's house in Great Pagwell. So whenever I want ideas for Professor Branestawm's inventions, I just pop along to Pagwell and ask the Professor his very self. But his explanations don't make my head go round and round as they do Colonel Dedshott's, thank goodness. But you have to be careful getting there, because the tunnel runs under Commander Hardaport's house next door, and he keeps anchors and other nautical jewellery in the tunnel which you're apt to trip over, as it isn't as wide as the Channel Tunnel hopes to be.

Born in London. Lives in Staines, Middlesex.

Books in Puffin:
DRIBBLESOME TEAPOTS
INCREDIBLE ADVENTURES OF PROFESSOR BRANESTAWM
PROFESSOR BRANESTAWM'S TREASURE HUNT
THE PECULIAR TRIUMPH OF PROFESSOR BRANESTAWM
PUFFIN BOOK OF MAGIC
THE HOME-MADE DRAGON
PROFESSOR BRANESTAWM'S DICTIONARY

This playground is the one where Robin and Kate met the strange, pale little boy they called 'Squib.' A lonely path goes down to the park from our house, with gardens on one side and a wood on the other, and when my children were younger they were a bit scared of it. The wood isn't much of a wood, just a tangle of old trees in the grounds of a big hotel (Turner's Tower in the story) but it seemed dark and mysterious to them. And one day, when a boy in a leather jacket with The Wild One painted in white on the back, jumped out from the trees and threatened them with a knife, it became a frightening place, too.

Parks are places where quite small children often go on their own and where things sometimes happen to them that grown ups know nothing about. My children didn't tell me about The Wild One for almost a year and, when they did, I remembered how I had once played in the park near my home and done things and met people I never mentioned to my mother. Remembering this, walking down our dark path, I began to wonder what would happen if Robin and Kate and Sammy and Prue met a strange, pale little boy in this park where my children played now . . .

Nina Bawden

Born in London.
Lives in Weybridge,
Surrey.

Books in Puffin:
A HANDFUL OF THIEVES
THE RUNAWAY SUMMER
ON THE RUN
THE WHITE HORSE GANG
THE WITCH'S DAUGHTER
SQUIB
CARRIE'S WAR

Hungerford Bridge is my favourite place in London. It isn't a road bridge, just a railway bridge, with a little footpath hanging on the side. The River Thames makes a sweeping turn, and you can see London curving around you all the way to St. Pauls. This is where Bill and Julie in Fireweed stood and watched London all on fire on the night of the great air-raid. Of course the Festival Hall is here now, instead of the old shot-tower, and lots of new offices like upended matchboxes, blotting out the spires of Wren churches that used to be the highest things in London except St. Pauls itself. And I don't suppose the Discovery was tied up to the embankment during the war. But even though it's changed, its still the 'Londonest' place I know. Come and find it if you visit London. There's a flight of steps up to beside Charing Cross underground station.

Jill Paton Walsh

Brought up in North Finchley
Lives in Richmond, Surrey

Books in Puffin:
FIREWEED
HENGEST'S TABLE
WORDHOARD (with Kevin Crossley-Holland)
THE DOLPHIN CROSSING

Although I have been to most of the places about which I write—Greece and Troy, Egypt and so on—I can't get back to them when I'm actually writing, except with the aid of books. And I'm lucky to have a positive magician's cave of books, an old library which was built and started nearly 300 years ago by an ancestor of mine, but which now holds mainly the books which I have collected, and which I read and reread, and use again and again when I am writing. Books about ancient Greece and books by ancient Greek authors, who wrote the tales which I retell; but also books by favourite authors such as Andrew Lang and Lewis Carroll, Rider Haggard and Rudyard Kipling and C. S. Lewis; and many others whose lives I have written or whose books I have selected and edited; for, like Lang himself, 'the books I loved I love them still.'

Roger Lancelyn Green

Born in Norwich.
Lives in Wirral, Cheshire.

Books in Puffin:
KING ARTHUR AND HIS KNIGHTS
   OF THE ROUND TABLE
MYTHS OF THE NORSEMEN
THE TALE OF TROY
TALES OF ANCIENT EGYPT
TALES OF THE GREEK HEROES
THE LUCK OF TROY
A BOOK OF DRAGONS (ed.)   *see next page*

WHAT DO YOU WANT?

Some connections and reiterations by

REMY CHARLIP

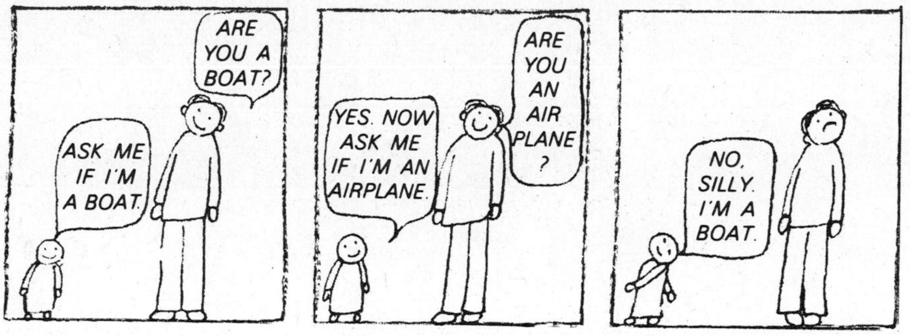

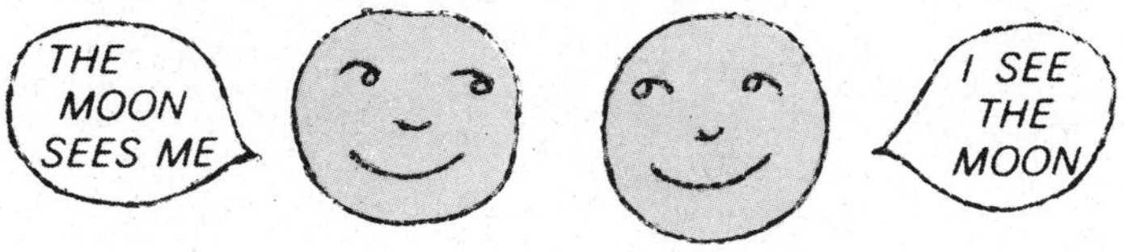

ASK ME IF I'M A BOAT.
ARE YOU A BOAT?
YES. NOW ASK ME IF I'M AN AIRPLANE.
ARE YOU AN AIR PLANE?
NO, SILLY. I'M A BOAT.

THE MOON SEES ME
I SEE THE MOON

I THINK OF YOU EVERYTIME I THINK OF YOU EVERYTIME I THINK OF YOU EVERYTIME I THINK OF YOU EVERYTIME I THINK OF YOU EVERYTIME I THINK OF YOU EVERYTIME I THINK OF YOU EVERYTIME I THINK OF YOU EVERYTIME I THINK OF YOU EVERYTIME I THINK OF YOU EVERYTIME I THINK OF YOU EVERYTIME I THINK OF YOU EVERYTIME

I AM WHAT I AM WHAT I AM WHAT I AM WHAT I AM WHAT I AM WHAT I AM WHAT I AM WHAT I AM WHAT I AM WHAT I AM WHAT I AM WHAT I AM WHAT I AM WHAT I AM WHAT I AM

WHAT IS MINE IS YOURS AND WHAT IS YOURS IS MINE AND WHAT IS MINE IS YOURS AND WHAT IS YOURS IS MINE AND WHAT IS MINE IS YOURS AND WHAT IS YOURS IS MINE AND

AROUND AND ROUND AND ROUND AND ROUND AND ROUND

I
WANT
A
SANDWICH
WITH
SOME
HAM
AND
SOME
CHEESE
AND
SOME
BUTTER
AND
SOME
MUSTARD
AND
SOME
SALT
AND
SOME
PEPPER
AND
SOME
TOMATO
AND
SOME
LETTUCE
AND
SOME
MAYONNAISE
AND
SOME
KETCHUP
AND
SOME
RELISH
AND
YES
SOME
BREAD

I WANT A SMALL PIECE OF STRING WITH AN ANT ON IT CARRYING A SMALL PIECE OF STRING WITH A WORM ON IT CARRYING A SMALL PIECE OF STRING WITH A BIRD ON IT CARRYING A SMALL PIECE OF STRING WITH A CAT ON IT CARRYING A SMALL PIECE OF STRING WITH A DOG ON IT CARRYING A SMALL PIECE OF STRING WITH A COW ON IT CARRYING A SMALL PIECE OF STRING WITH A HORSE ON IT CARRYING A SMALL PIECE OF STRING WITH A RHINOCEROS ON IT CARRYING A SMALL PIECE OF STRING WITH AN ELEPHANT ON IT CARRYING A SMALL PIECE OF STRING WITH A DINOSAUR ON IT CARRYING A SMALL PIECE OF STRING WITH A SMALL PIECE OF STRING ON IT.

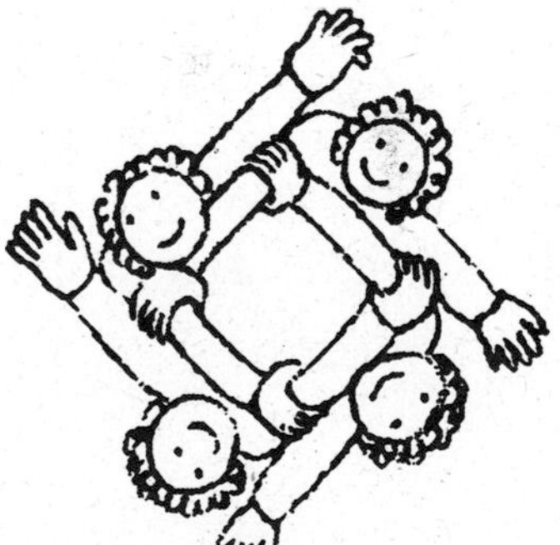

I WANT A CHOCOLATE COVERED CHERRY
AND A CHOCOLATE COVERED EASTER EGG
AND A CHOCOLATE COVERED VALENTINE
AND A CHOCOLATE COVERED ICE CREAM CONE
AND A CHOCOLATE COVERED BIRTHDAY CAKE
AND A CHOCOLATE COVERED CHRISTMAS TREE
AND A CHOCOLATE COVERED SNOWMAN
AND A CHOCOLATE COVERED BICYCLE
AND SOME CHOCOLATE COVERED SPAGHETTI.

taken from Arm in Arm, Perpetua Press.

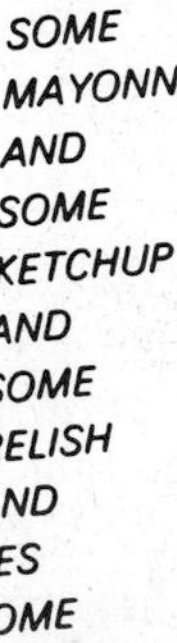

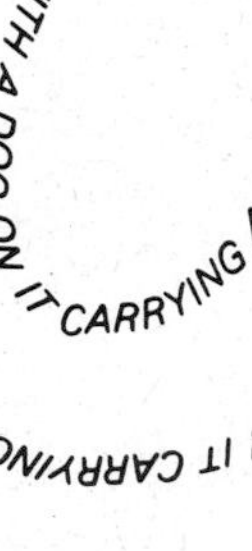

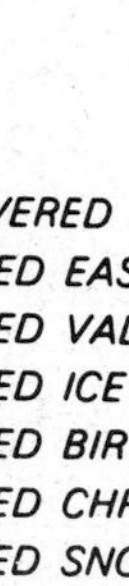

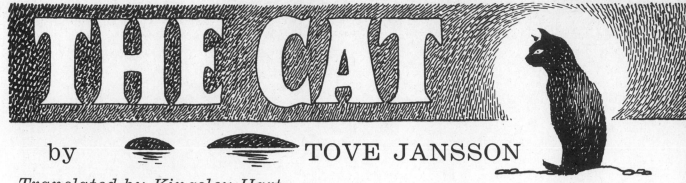

THE CAT

by TOVE JANSSON

Translated by Kingsley Hart

The cat was very small when she arrived and could only drink milk from a baby's bottle. It was a mercy that Sophia's old one was still in the attic! At first the kitten curled up in the tea-cosy to keep warm, but when she could stand she slept in Sophia's bed in the playhouse. She had her own pillow next to hers.

She was a grey fisherman's cat and she grew quickly. One day she left the playhouse and moved into the cottage to spend her nights with the dirty dishes in the box under the bed, for by then she already had a mind of her own. Sophia carried the cat back to the playhouse, and did all she could to make her like her, but the more love she gave, the quicker the cat was back with the dishes again. And when the box was full up, so that there was no room for her, the cat made a terrible row and somebody had to do the washing up. Her name was Ma Petite, and she was called Mappie.

'Cats are funny things,' said Sophia. 'The more you love them the less they like you.'

'That's very true,' said Granny. 'And what can one do about it?'

'Why, go on loving!' Sophia insisted. 'You just love more and more.'

Granny sighed and said nothing.

So Sophia carried Mappie around to all the nice places that a cat might like, but she looked this way and that and then wandered off. She was hugged and squeezed until she was almost flat, bore it all very politely and then crept in among the dishes again. When she was subjected to earnest confidences she just turned her yellow eyes away, and nothing in the world seemed to interest her apart from sleeping and eating.

'You know what?' said Sophia, 'sometimes I think I hate Mappie. I just can't go on loving her any longer, and I think about her all the time!'

Week after week the cat was followed everywhere by Sophia. She spoke to her gently, gave her tenderness and understanding, and only once or twice did she lose her temper and tug her tail. Then Mappie would spit at her and disappear under the house and come out later with a better appetite than ever, and then sleep longer than usual, curled up in her remote softness with one paw prettily over her nose.

Sophia stopped playing and started having nightmares. She could think of nothing but the cat and the fact that she wouldn't show any affection. All this time Mappie was growing into a thin and wild little cat and one fine June night she didn't return to the

Drawings by Tove Jansson

box with the dirty dishes. In the morning she came into the cottage and stretched herself. First her front legs, sticking her bottom in the air, then her hind legs, then she shut her eyes and began to sharpen her claws on the rocking-chair. After that she jumped onto the bed for a nap.

She's started to hunt, thought Granny.

She was right. The very next morning the cat came in and laid a small greyish-yellow bird on the doorstep. The bird's neck had been neatly bitten right through and a few red drops of blood rested prettily on its shiny feathers. Sophia turned pale, and stared unflinchingly at the murdered bird. She walked past the murderer Mappie with short stiff side-steps, then turned and rushed out.

Later on Granny mentioned the curious fact that wild animals, cats for example, don't understand the difference between rats and birds.

'Then they're stupid,' Sophia said curtly. 'Rats are nasty and birds are nice. I don't think I shall talk to Mappie for three days.' And so she didn't talk to her cat any longer.

Every night the cat went into the forest and every morning she caught her prey and carried it into the cottage in order to be admired and every time the bird was thrown into the sea. After a little while Sophia began to stand outside the window and shout: 'Is it all right to come in? Has the corpse been cleared away?' She punished Mappie and increased her own suffering by showing a consuming cynicism. Sometimes she would shout: 'Have you washed away the blood?' Or: 'How many have been murdered today?' And breakfast wasn't the same as it used to be.

It's one thing to know that a pool of blood exists but quite another thing to actually see it so it was a great relief when Mappie eventually learnt to conceal her crimes. She had probably got tired of all the shouting and the fuss, and perhaps she thought that the family were eating her birds. Then one morning when Granny was smoking her first cigarette on the veranda she dropped her cigarette-holder through a crack in the floor. When she lifted one of the floor-boards she saw what Mappie had been doing: a neat little row of small birds gnawed to the bone. Of course she knew that the cat was still hunting and couldn't give it up, but the next time Mappie rubbed against her leg as she went past she moved away and whispered: 'You cunning little devil!'

'I say,' said Sophia, 'I wish that Mappie had never been born. Or that I had never been born. That would have been better.'

'So you're still not talking to each other?' Granny asked.

'Not a word,' Sophia replied. 'I just don't know what to do. What's the point of forgiving her when she doesn't care whether I do or not!' And Granny couldn't think of a thing to say.

Mappie became a wild cat and very seldom came into the cottage. She was the same colour as the island, a

light greyish-yellow with striped shading like a rock, or sunlight on a sandy bottom under water. When she crept over the field by the shore her movements were like the passage of wind through the grass. She stood in the brushwood on the look-out for hours, a motionless silhouette, two pointed ears against the sunset that suddenly vanished . . . and something squeaked, just once. She crawled in under the low pine branches which hugged the ground and washed herself voluptuously when the sun came out. She was a perfectly happy cat, but she didn't share a thing with anybody. On hot days she stretched herself out on the smooth rock and sometimes she ate grass and brought up her own hair quite calmly in the way cats do. And what she did in-between nobody knew.

One Saturday, the Jonssons from the village came to tea. Sophia went down to the beach and looked at their boat. It was big, and full of bags and jerry-cans and baskets, and in one of the baskets a cat was mewing. Sophia lifted the lid and the cat licked her hand. He was large and white and had a fat face. The cat didn't stop purring when she lifted him out and carried him ashore.

'So you've found the cat,' said Annie Jonsson. 'He's a good cat but he doesn't catch mice, so we thought we would give him to the Peterssons.'

Sophia sat down on the bed with the heavy cat in her lap, and he purred the whole time. He was soft and warm and submissive.

Things were arranged quite easily with a bottle of rum as a token payment for the exchange. Mappie was caught and didn't understand what it was all about before the Jonssons' boat was well on the way to the village.

The new cat was called Whitey. He ate perch and he liked being stroked. He moved into the playhouse and every night he slept in Sophia's arms and every morning he came to breakfast and went on sleeping on the bed next to the stove. If the sun was shining he curled up on the warm rock.

'Not there!' shouted Sophia. 'That's Mappie's place!' She carried the cat a little further away, he licked her nose and obediently curled up on the new spot.

With every day the summer became more and more beautiful, a long succession of calm, blue days. Every night Whitey slept with his nose against Sophia's cheek.

'There's something funny about me,' said Sophia. 'I think nice weather all the time is boring.'

'Do you?' Granny said. 'Then you're exactly like Grandpa, he liked storms, too.' But before she had time to say anything else about Grandpa, Sophia had walked away.

And very gradually the wind got up, cautiously at first during the night, but by morning there was a good old sou'wester lashing the rocks with foam.

'Wake up!' Sophia whispered, 'Wake up, my darling! There's a storm.'

Whitey purred and stretched his warm legs in all directions, and the sheets were covered with cat hair.

'Jump up!' Sophia shouted, 'There's a storm!' And the cat just turned over on his fat stomach. Sophia got terribly angry quite suddenly, kicked open the door and flung the cat out into the gale and watched him flatten his ears. 'Hunt!' she screamed. '*Do* something! Be a *cat*!' Then she started to cry and ran to the guest-room and banged on the door.

'What's the matter now?' asked Granny.

'I want Mappie back!' Sophia shouted.

'You know what it will be like, don't you?'

'Awful!' said Sophia seriously. 'But Mappie is the one I love.' So they exchanged cats again.

THE STRANGE AFFAIR of the WATTLE-U-EAT

by BRENDA JOHNSON

provisions - Peter Edwards

Young Percy P. Puffin,
A bird of great brain
Who lived with his parents
In Hollybush Lane
Was anxious to give all
His family a treat,
So he built them a thing called
A WATTLE-U-EAT.

'It supplies,' he said proudly
'Lunch, dinner or tea.
'It's ready for serving
And everything's free !'
They all gathered round it to
Press down the button
And out popped a nicely-cooked
Shoulder of mutton.

Followed by spinach, and
    slices of ham,
Six biscuits, two loaves and
Some strawberry jam.
'How useful,' said Mother
As out came a bunch
Of spring onions. 'These things will
Do nicely for lunch.'

But before they could move, or
Their Mother was able
To set the things out on
The dining-room table,

The WATTLE-U-EAT was
Beginning to pour
Food in great quantities
Over the floor.

Parsnips and turnips
With mushrooms and steak
Followed by trifle
And coconut cake.
Dumplings in gravy
With carrots and peas
Spaghetti and sausages,
Camembert cheese.
Rabbit and chicken
And savoury pies
Of various flavours
And varying size.

Food that was frozen and
Food wrapped in packets.
Beans, macaroni
Potatoes in jackets.
Foods of all colours
And different shapes.
Radishes, peaches
And muscatel grapes.

They started to store all the
Food in the larder
But finding the space became
Harder and harder.
They filled up the attic
The landing and stairs
With oranges, apples
And William pears.

The lettuces, cabbage
And peppermint creams
Were piled on the floor
Nearly reaching the beams.

Mother said mildly:
'I don't wish to seem
Ungrateful or rude but
I warn you I'll scream
If just one more pilchard
Or plateful of meat
Emerges from Percy P.'s
WATTLE-U-EAT.'

Said Father : 'At giving out
Food we can't fault it,
But surely it's time you
Explained how to halt it ?'

Poor Percy P. Puffin
Had turned rather red.
'I'm afraid that it's only
Just entered my head.'
He said to them all as
He gave a slight cough.
'There isn't a lever
For turning it off.'

He took off the back
Examined the works
And then as he gave it
A couple of jerks
The machine began shaking
And with a loud hum
Food started returning
The way it had come.

They gazed down at Percy
With wide-open beaks.
They cried : 'But that means
It might go on for weeks.'
And as though the machine had
Heard just what they'd said
It gave out a new load
Of thinly sliced bread.

'But here's the solution,
Said Percy P. Puffin,
Ducking to miss being
Hit by a muffin.
'I think to the problem
An answer I've found
I'll just set it going
The other way round.

The ice-creams and jellies
The rhubarb and custard
The boiled eggs and salad
And hot-dogs with mustard.
The olives and cherries
In gigantic numbers
The sardines and kippers
The pickled cucumbers.

And just as it took in the
Last apple tartlet
The WATTLE-U-EAT fell
To bits on the carpet.

Percy looked round and
Was forced to confess
That the house had got into
A bit of a mess.

The machine ran so fast that
In under an hour
It sucked up the last of
The self-raising flour.
Very soon after to
Percy's relief
It swallowed a rather
Large sirloin of beef.

Although he got help cleaning
Some of the others
From most of his sisters
And two of his brothers.

By working quite hard with
A mop and a broom
It took him five hours just
To clear up one room

They'd finished at last
At the end of the day
When Percy announced he
Had something to say.

'And never again,' vowed young
Percy P. Puffin
'Will I ever attempt to get
Somefin' for nuffin'.'

THAT AWFUL BOY
by Geoffrey Trease

Drawings by Mel Calman

'That awful boy!'

I never actually heard them call me that to my face, but the words must often have formed upon their furiously-bitten lips and in their turmoiled minds.

Because—I see it now—I *was*. I must have been.

My poor father must have thought it, for one. Imagine. Just before my thirteenth birthday, being a bookish lad, I won a scholarship at my school. Dad was pleased, if a bit dazed. The family tradition was all for sport. My elder brothers sped down the wing, fleet as stags, clutching rugger balls to their muddy chests or bowled out batsmen with slow, devilish cunning.

So, wishing to reward me for my own odd sort of success, my father asked:

'Would you like a cricket-bat or a bicycle?'

His face may be imagined when his unnatural and incomprehensible offspring answered like a flash:

'No, Dad, but I'd like a typewriter.'

Schoolboys in those days just didn't have typewriters. But very soon *I* did for my father was a broad-minded parent.

It was IMMENSE. It looked like one of those seige-engines they dragged up to the walls of a medieval city to hurl two-ton rocks at the enemy. Still, somehow we got it up to my little attic bedroom.

For years I had been writing stories. Even before I *could* write, if you know what I mean. Dad brought home huge unused desk diaries from his office, and before I could form real words I used to cover the blank pages with lines of squiggle, fiercely muttering my breath-taking narrative as the meaningless pencil moved along.

Years of real writing had followed. Dozens of penny notebooks filled with blood-curdling adventures, shipwrecks, savages, mutinies, treasure – whatever – I'd been reading in print or seeing at the cinema.

Who should I sell the film rights to?

The typewriter ribbon produced my masterpieces in a rich, blurred purple, as though the ink had been made from the blood of Roman emperors.

I still have some of those typewritten stories. I brought out a paper, *The British Boys' Magazine*, in a single copy which I made my family and friends pay a halfpenny a time to borrow. I suppose I never thought of doubling or tripling the circulation by using carbon paper. Anyhow, it would have been so boring to copy the illustrations which I drew in ink and water-colour.

Dad was much perturbed that I spent all those hours upstairs, pounding out my stories. He murmured much of 'fresh air'. I ought to have been chasing a ball of some kind, according to season.

But when not writing stories I was usually reading. Anything. We hadn't much choice in those days. There were no Puffins. There were plenty of hard-backs in the bookshops, of course, for Christmas presents and school prizes, but they would seem a stodgy lot to the boys and girls of today. There was a children's library, but my parents wouldn't let me use it. Dirt, germs, ugh!

So I read whatever I could find, suitable or unsuitable. I read yards and yards of

91

Shakespeare in teeny, sight-spoiling print, two columns to the dusty page. I even *learnt* yards of it by heart, acting it to myself in private, especially the gory bits, the murders and suicides. *Hamlet*, *Macbeth*, *Julius Caesar*, the lot.

Sometimes I craved an audience, Mother obliged. She would sit in her armchair while I orated at her as I had heard Sir Frank Benson and other great actors declaim in our own local theatre. I would drink imaginary poison or thrust

my dagger (a school ruler) into my hopeless heart. I died, as they say, a thousand deaths.

Once my long-suffering parent made a near-fatal mistake. Nervously, she laughed in the wrong place. (I think I was Macbeth, at that moment, working myself up to murder King Duncan.) Worked up I certainly was, for at that untimely laugh I broke off and laid furious unfilial hands not on Duncan but on my mother.

'He took me by the throat,' she reported afterwards – quite cheerfully, almost admiringly, certainly not crossly – 'he took me by the throat and shook me, like a terrier shaking a rat.'

Poor Mother! Surely she must have said to *herself*, however confidentially, 'That awful boy!'

Some of my schoolmasters would certainly have shared that view.

There was, for instance, 'Beaky' Bridge, who gave me the love of history which I have never lost.

'Beaky' had not only a prominent nose, but an angry squawk (when a pupil annoyed him) that would have aroused envy from a whole aviary of parrakeets.

Inattention he could not abide. If he saw a boy dozing he would lift the flap of his own desk, seize one of the hard little fives balls he kept there and hurl the missile down the long classroom with unerring aim.

It was lucky that his aim *was* unerring, because he meant to miss the boy's head and it was rather important that he should. Fives balls are deadly things. They used to whizz over our heads – it was like the Battle of Trafalgar – and crash against the wall.

He didn't need to throw at me. I was attentive enough, because I liked history and lapped up every amusing word that fell from his crooked lips. He terrified you, but he was first-class entertainment and a great teacher. It was largely because of the history he taught me that I won the afore-mentioned scholarship.

Well, imagine. Next term I went into his form. He'd got his eye on me. Bright in his pet subject. Suitably trained and groomed over the next few years, I'd notch up a university scholarship at Oxford. I'd be another of Beaky's successes. And now calamity . . .

Beaky took our names, made up his register, dished out notebooks, and the like. Then he ran his beady eye over us and squawked with infinite contempt:

'Who are the *Greek* merchants?'

Very few boys learned Greek, three or four each year out of about thirty, and those almost exclu-

GREEK HISTORY

sively the boys who had already decided to become parsons. The point was, if you took Greek, you had to give up History. So Beaky didn't much like the few boys who deserted him and chose Greek instead.

'Let's be having you!' he cried in blood-chilling tones. And four tremulous hands went up. Mine was one. Most reluctantly. For the school had persuaded my father that I should go on with Latin, begin Greek, and forsake History.

It is embarrassing, even nowadays, when I get up to lecture to a meeting and the chairman has said something nice about me as a 'historical writer' – and I have to confess to my learned-looking audience that no one taught me any English History after I was thirteen.

It was worse than embarrassing when I faced Beaky that morning. '*You!*' he said, and the squawk was strangled in his throat. He just stared, and his bony jaw dropped. It was like Caesar when his best friend came up and stabbed him. 'You . . .' was all he said,

but his bleak eyes added 'awful boy'.

The Greek master was new, and in his own way just as alarming. We went to him later that same morning, a shy little foursome. He took out his pen, and said, 'I'll have your names first. Alphabetically.'

I was the third. 'Trease, sir,' I said. And the fourth boy said, 'Twelvetrees, sir!'

I thought the man would explode. In a dangerous controlled tone, he said, 'Is this your idea of a joke?'

'No, sir,' we bleated, 'they really *are* our names.'

I tell the story because it may help people to realize that my name is pronounced quite differently from that of the late Henry Treece, with whom – maddeningly for booksellers and librarians – I am so often confused.

In the end I was quite glad to have learned Greek. However cock-eyed it may sound, writing Greek taught me to write better English. Many years later, my own thirteen-year-old daughter, Jocelyn, decided without any urging from me that she would like to study the language. It was then that I sat down and wrote *The Crown of Violet*, dedicated to 'J. and her friends who chose Greek' and I wanted to show them quickly, while they were still wrestling with the awkward alphabet and the gruesome grammar, what a world of enchantment ancient Athens had been.

I was lucky in my teachers. For now there came to the school a young English master, Garry Hogg, only a few years older than myself, and destined himself to win a reputation as a writer – though, strangely, he did not start until after I did. Garry must sometimes have thought of me as 'that awful boy'. but for a different reason.

In the enthusiasm of his first term, finding that I (now sixteen) was keen on books and writing, he gave me an open invitation to drop in at his lodgings in the evening and borrow from his own shelves, but could hardly have foreseen that I should be knocking on his door sometimes twice in one week, to talk or show him my latest poem. No wonder he got married six months later and bought a house three miles distant at the top of

Now for VOL.2.

Please Sir —
Can I be excused
boredom?

a punishing hill. But he and his wife still invited me, bless them.

'Coverdale' they called their house, and fitted a nameplate on the gate with separate letters bought from Woolworth's. Another boy and I spent a thoughtful few minutes with pencil and paper. Then we crept along in the summer darkness with a screwdriver, removed the name-plate, and put it back reading, 'A CLEVER DO'.

Within twenty-four hours I'd received a postcard in Garry's minuscule handwriting. '*Stout work. G.L.H.*' He knew, all right.

Then I departed for Oxford, and was a 'boy' no more, but no less tiresome, I expect, to those who had to cope with me. For it was at Oxford that I first burnt my boats in a big way, when I decided that the schoolmaster's life was not for me, and writing was the thing. Which it still is – after all these desperate and comic years.

The Disappearing King

The King of Hearts is clearly seen to be among the other cards of a pack, yet when the cards are dealt out on the table the King of Hearts has completely vanished.

To do this you make a special trick card. Take the King of Hearts and some other card, say the five of spades. Cut a thin strip from the top of the five of spades, thus making it a shorter card than the others in the pack. Stick this five of spades to the King of Hearts with a little paste just at the bottom. You now have a double card with the short five of spades in front, that can be opened a little way at the top.

Put this trick card into the pack. Now show the pack and holding it in your left hand, riffle the cards at the top, letting them go past like the pages of a book. When you come to the trick card the short card will pass but cause the riffle to stop at the King of Hearts. Draw attention to the king then riffle the rest of the cards.

Now say you will make the King of Hearts disappear. Count the cards out onto the table, faces upwards. The King of Hearts is of course hidden by the five of spades that is stuck to it and so seems to have vanished. And there are only fifty-one cards instead of fifty-two.

Making the trick card

Five of spades cut a little short at the top.

King of Hearts.

The two cards are stuck together here

You won't Believe it but . . .

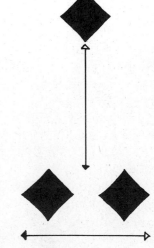

This distance . . .

is exactly the same as this distance.

94

More authors tell you about their favourite places.

Elisabeth Beresford

The bit of Wimbledon Common that you can see (below) means a lot to me, because it was right in the middle of it that I discovered the Wombles. Or perhaps it would be more accurate to say that they discovered me.

The children and I had been nipping over to the Common for years. My daughter Kate takes beautiful photographs of Queen's Mere, birds and the squirrels. My son Marcus learnt to ride his bike here. And one Christmas we lost a brand new kite . . . it snapped its string and away it went with us after it, but we never did find out where it came to earth.

Perhaps the Wombles found it do you think?

I was born in Paris, hence the reason for my name being spelt Elisabeth. And as my father didn't believe in any kind of bureaucracy I was never registered anywhere, so legally I don't exist. . .

Born in France

Lives in Wandsworth, London

Books in Puffin:
THE INVISIBLE WOMBLE
   and Other Stories (Young Puffin)
THE WANDERING WOMBLES
WOMBLES IN DANGER

Cynthia Harnett

The photo (above) was taken in the churchyard at EWELME in Oxfordshire, the village of THE WRITING ON THE HEARTH where Stephen lived and faced his great adventure. Beyond the wall are the roofs of the same school, which he attended 500 years ago and the almshouses where his old friend Doggett lived. Doggett had fought at Agincourt; he had an endless fund of stories and his bright eyes missed nothing that went on round him. In the church, just out of the picture, lies Stephen's beloved lady, Dame Alice Chaucer, serene upon her lovely tomb.

Further away are the wooded hills where outlaws poached deer from the Lord of Ewelme. There, also, lived an old woman said to be a witch. Was she or was she not? Stephen did not believe it. But on the answer to that question the whole story turns.

Born in Kensington, London

Lives in Henley-on-Thames, Oxfordshire

Books in Puffin:
THE GREAT HOUSE
THE LOAD OF UNICORN
THE WOOL-PACK
RING OUT BOW BELLS!
THE WRITING ON THE HEARTH

I've always had this passion for trees—felt they were beautiful, magical, live things—that by just touching them you can draw a kind of power out of the world itself. All the poems and stories I liked best when I was little had trees in them—Hushabye Baby, the Mowgli *books, full of jungle and creepers, Tarzan, Robin Hood —remember the lovely banyan in which the Swiss Family Robinson lived, with honeycomb in its hollow trunk?*

I was lucky, for our garden had so many climbable trees—beech, willow, laurel, cherry, fig, apple, pear, plum, walnut; I can still remember every branch of that walnut tree. You had to swarm up the rope of the swing to get into it, and then you could climb very high indeed and see right over our house roof.

Various trees have grown into my stories—a live family tree, and a stolen quince tree (based on a true episode) and a laurel that belonged to the moon goddess, and a lilac in a lake, and the fern-covered oak from which Arabis heard the thieves plotting in The Whispering Mountain, *and of course* The Cuckoo Tree, *a real tree that I still sometimes climb. But oddly enough, the weird-looking hollow horizontal oak in this picture is one that I never climb. It's such a marvellous tree that it deserves a whole book to itself. So now I suppose I shall have to write it.*

Borne in Rye, Sussex. Lives in Petworth and New York.

Joan Aiken

Books in Puffin: THE WOLVES OF WILLOUGHBY CHASE
BLACK HEARTS IN BATTERSEA
NIGHT BIRDS ON NANTUCKET
A SMALL PINCH OF WEATHER
THE WHISPERING MOUNTAIN
THE CUCKOO TREE
THE KINGDOM UNDER THE SEA
ALL BUT A FEW (74)
A HARP OF FISHBONES (Dec 74)

Hammersmith Bridge means a lot of different things to me. It is strange to think what a barrier even a little river like the Thames used to be, and for how long, and then how our ancestors stitched the south bank to the north. When the iron bridges began to be built they used the new material with frivolous abandon. Hammersmith Bridge, when you first come to it, looks like the drawbridge of some fairy castle. It is old now. When something heavy crosses, it groans and shudders beneath the weight, as though its iron bones had rheumatism. I put it into one of my books, The Devil's Children, *but didn't make as much fuss about it as I might have, because I wanted to get on with the story. It's the place where Nicky watches the river and wonders whether she could sail to France, just before the Sikhs start the engine of an abandoned bus and she rushes to attack them, and thus becomes their 'canary'.*

Born in Africa (within sound of the Victoria Falls)
Lives in London and Hampshire

Books in Puffin: THE WEATHERMONGER } the
HEARTSEASE   } 'Changes'
THE DEVIL'S CHILDREN   } trilogy
EMMA TUPPER'S DIARY
THE DANCING BEAR
THE GIFT

Peter Dickinson

96

Tale The Third

THE NIGHT WATCHMAN
AND THE CROCODILE

by Russell Hoban

Illustrated by Fritz Wegner

Is now the only time there is?

THE night watchman was made of wood. He wore a black coat, a top hat, and a red kerchief, and he carried a ladder and a long-handled candle snuffer. He was evidently the sort of night watchman who lit and snuffed out the candles in the street lamps and called out the hours in whatever time and place he had come from. His real job was burning incense. His whole hollow body was detachable from the base on which he stood, and when a cone of burning incense was placed on the base and his body put back on top of it the fragrant smoke came out of his open mouth. He called out the hours as well, of course, but no one understood what he was saying. He was totally foreign in speech as well as in appearance, and the clock on the wall could not even recognize the names of the hours called out by the incense-burning wooden night watchman.

The crocodile, tin and handsome, red and green and yellow, rolled on little rubber wheels with a comfortable whirring sound, moving his green legs and opening and closing his splendidly toothed red mouth as he crossed the pattern of the oriental carpet. For years he had said to himself that he was going to compose a poem for the literary quarterly edited by the spinster mouse who lived behind the skirting board. 'I'm definitely going to do it,' he said. 'It's just a matter of waiting for the right time. It's in me. I have the talent. I have the confidence.'

'Half-past ten!' said the night watchman in his own language. He had not understood a word of what the crocodile had said. 'Something burns in me,' he said. 'What is it that burns in me?' No one had explained the incense and its heat and its fragrance to him. It was simply something that

97

happened inside him from time to time. 'Such a burning in me!' said the night watchman. 'Such a fragrance! I am burning, burning, burning to say something.'

'Of course,' said the crocodile, who in his turn understood nothing of what the night watchman said, 'for you life is simple. You are secure with your ladder and your candle snuffer. You are not especially burning to say anything; your fragrant smoke is enough for you. You have a working-class outlook, and you are happier because of it.'

'Burning to say something!' shouted the night watchman. 'It is in me, something to say!'

'You simply don't know how it is with literary people like me,' the crocodile went on. 'The waiting, waiting, waiting for that perfect time!'

The night watchman had burned more incense than usual that evening. He was giddy with the fragrance and the heat of it, words danced in his head. In all the words of his own language he found nothing to say, but as the hours passed his mind became full of the sounds of the language the crocodile spoke so flowingly. Unknown words danced in his head. Eleven o'clock came, half-past eleven. Then it was midnight, and there was that tiny buzzing pause while the clock gathered itself to strike twelve times.

'NOW IS THE ONLY TIME THERE IS!' shouted the night watchman in the crocodile's language, in words he did not know the meaning of.

'What's that?' said the startled crocodile as the clock finished its twelve strokes.

The night watchman could not say it again. The words had vanished from his mind. His incense had burnt out. But the crocodile had heard him well enough.

'Is it?' said the crocodile. 'Is now the only time there is?' He ran back and forth upon the oriental carpet,

whirring excitedly. Without further delay he composed a strong poem, went quickly to the hole in the skirting board, and recited it to the spinster mouse editor.

'This is very good indeed,' she said. 'We'll run it in the next issue. I never thought you'd do it.'

'That night watchman is extraordinary,' said the crocodile. He ran back across the carpet and stopped in front of the night watchman. 'Tell me more,' he said. 'I feel that I have much to learn from you.'

But the night watchman's incense was burnt out. He had forgotten what he had said, and he had never understood the words to begin with. In the evenings that passed he never got hot enough to speak that language again.

The crocodile, however, remembered his words. He went on making up poems, and in time there were enough of them to fill a book which was published by the spinster mouse.

A bookseller down in Porthcawl
Whose shop was exceedingly smawl
Said 'I cannot find homes
For enormous great tomes,
So it's Puffins or nothing at awl'

ANIMAL CRACKS
by Puffineers

Why did the chicken cross the road?
Because the subway was closed.

First seal: Do you know the rumour about Noah?
Second seal: No.
First seal: Ark, ark, ark!

Man: Do you serve fish here?
Waiter: Yes, sir, we serve anyone.

What did the Spanish farmer say to his hen?
Olé.

Why do Swiss cows wear bells?
Because their horns don't work

Greenhorn: Do you get fur from a skunk?
Hunter: Yes sir! We get as fur from a skunk as possible!

One snake said to another snake: 'Lucky I'm not poisonous, I just bit my tongue.'

What's got a big mouth and is covered with flowers?
A hippypotamus.

There were two flies playing football in a saucer. A spider who came to watch them thought they were not playing well and said, 'You'd better play a good game tomorrow because you'll be playing in the cup!' (Sarah Walker, 9, Sussex)

What is black and white and black and white and black and white?
A Puffin falling down the stairs.

The Gibber

The Gibber is
  a curious pet
(or some would say
          a pest).
It gets inside
  your TV set
and there it makes
          its nest.

Its little teeth
  are strong as pliers.
Its claws are useful
          too.
It weaves a nest
  of coloured wires
with here and there
          a screw.

It joins the ends
  it doesn't want
into their old
          position,
but often gets them
  back to front—
it's not an elec-
      trician.

On sets infested
  by this pet
you see some curious
          views.
I know a tele-
  vision set
where Bosscat reads
          the News.

Commercials in
  particular
are apt to make
          you stare.
They say 'Put toothpaste
  in your car!'
'Put gravy on
          your hair!'

At dusk the gibber
  wakes and stirs
It's then you see
          the sight
Of Dougal keeping
  goal for Spurs
in Magic Football Night.

The last IMPOSSIBLE PET
by Peter Dickinson
Drawings by Raymond Briggs

THE UPSIDEDOWN MICE
Story by ROALD DAHL
and sort of written out and illustrated
by Antony Maitland

Once upon a time there lived an old man of 87 whose name was Labon. All his life he had been a quiet and peaceful person. He was very poor and very happy.

When Labon discovered that he had mice in his house, he did not at first bother himself greatly about it. But the mice multiplied.

They kept right on multiplying and finally there came a time when he could stand it no longer.

"This is too much," he said. "This really is going a bit too far."

He hobbled out of the house and down the road to a shop where he bought himself some mousetraps, a piece of cheese and some glue.

When he got home, he put the glue on the underneath of the mousetraps and stuck them to the ceiling. Then he baited them carefully with pieces of cheese and set them to go off.

That night when the mice came out of their holes and saw the mousetraps on the ceiling, they thought it a tremendous joke. They walked around on the floor, nudging each other and pointing up with their front paws and roaring with laughter. After all it was pretty silly, mousetraps on the ceiling.

When Labon came down the next morning and saw that there were no mice caught in the traps, he smiled but said nothing.

He took a chair and put glue on the bottom of its' legs and stuck it upsidedown to the ceiling, near the mousetraps.

He did the same with the table, the television set and the lamp. He took everything that was on the floor and stuck it upsidedown on the ceiling. He even put a little carpet up there.

TEE HEE

GLUB GLUE

Giggle giggle

He's out of his mind

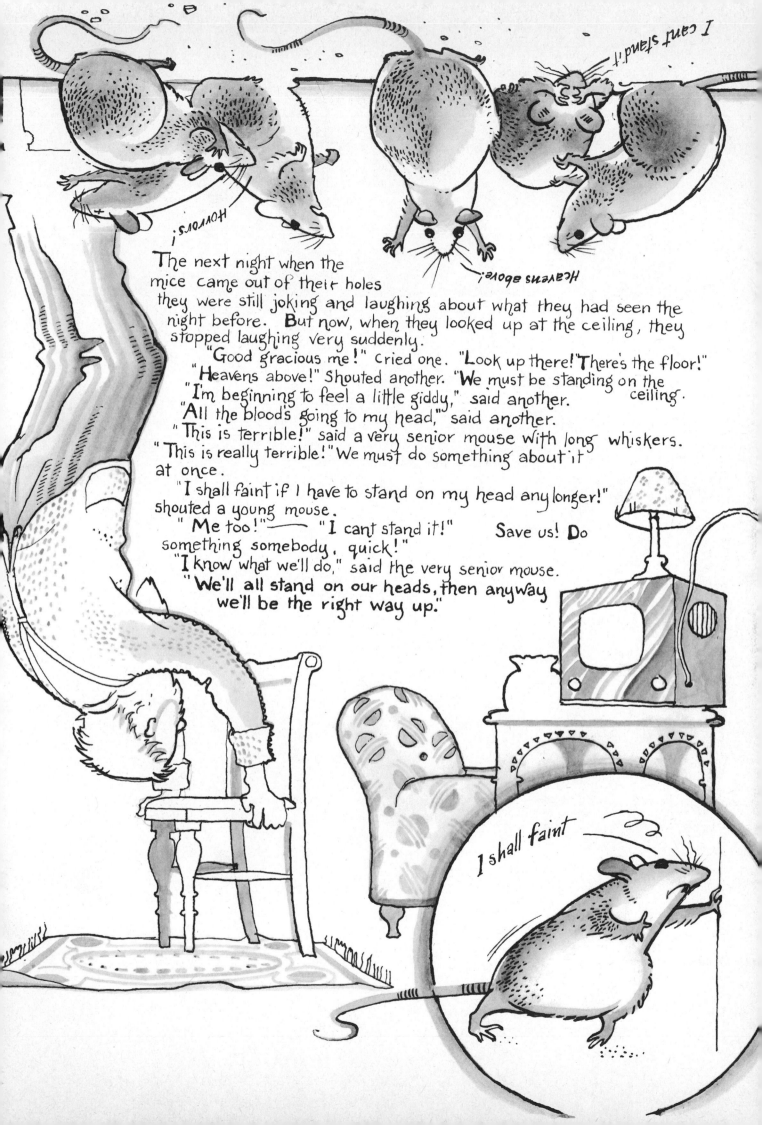

Horrors!

Heavens above!

I can't stand it

The next night when the
mice came out of their holes
they were still joking and laughing about what they had seen the
night before. But now, when they looked up at the ceiling, they
stopped laughing very suddenly.

"Good gracious me!" cried one. "Look up there! There's the floor!"

"Heavens above!" shouted another. "We must be standing on the
ceiling.

"I'm beginning to feel a little giddy," said another.

"All the blood's going to my head," said another.

"This is terrible!" said a very senior mouse with long whiskers.
"This is really terrible!" We must do something about it
at once.

"I shall faint if I have to stand on my head any longer!"
shouted a young mouse.

"Me too!" ——— "I can't stand it!"   Save us! Do
something somebody, quick!"

"I know what we'll do," said the very senior mouse.
"We'll all stand on our heads, then anyway
we'll be the right way up."

I shall faint

Obediently, they all stood on their heads, and after a long time, one by one, they fainted from a rush of blood to their brains.

When Labon came down the next morning the floor was littered with mice. Quickly he gathered them up and popped them all in a basket.

So the thing to remember is this :

WHENEVER THE WORLD SEEMS TO BE TERRIBLY UPSIDEDOWN, MAKE SURE YOU KEEP YOUR FEET FIRMLY ON THE GROUND.

PUFFIN POST

by GRISELDA GREAVES   drawings by JILL MCDONALD

FOR FIRST COMERS
Pin the break on the Puffin

PREPARATIONS: Draw a large picture of a Puffin without a beak and pin it on to a door. Make a separate beak with a drawing pin attached to it. Each guest is blindfolded, in turn, and has to pin the beak on to the right part of the picture. The pinhole is initialled and the guest with the best attempt wins.

FOR BREAKING THE ICE
Animal Crackers

PREPARATIONS: Hide six inch strands of different coloured wool all over the party rooms. Divide the guests into as many teams as there are colours of wool. Tell each team what colour to look for and which animal to imitate. One person from each team stays at base and the rest go hunting. As soon as anyone finds a strand of the right coloured wool he makes the right animal noise until the player waiting at base comes to collect the wool. The game ends after ten minutes. The team with the most wool wins.

Animal Pairs

PREPARATIONS: Make a list of as many animals as half the number of guests, i.e. if you have 20 guests you will need 10 animals. Make two cards of each animal on the list. (Draw a picture or write the name). As the guests arrive give each one a card. They must go round the room making the noise of the animal on their card until they find their mate. (Follow this game by another game involving pairs.)

FOR P'SUPER-BRIGHT PUFFINEERS
Bunyips

PREPARATIONS: Collect as many boxes of bits as there are guests. Each box should contain things like scraps of material, pins (preferably those with coloured heads as they are less easy to lose), buttons, cotton reels, paper, string, lengths of wool, etc. This game can be played in pairs.

Each player (or pair) is given a box of bits and ten minutes in which to make a creature called a bunyip. The best bunyip wins.

Puffin Charades

PREPARATIONS: Have ready a pencil and paper for each guest, and some old and odd clothes to dress up in.

Divide the guests into two teams. One team goes out of the room. Each team chooses a Puffin title. The teams prepare a scene where they use the first word of the title. They then prepare one for the other words and one in which they use the whole title. The team that is ready first, acts first. The other team is allowed three guesses to find the right title.

Variations: The title can be mimed by a team or by one person.

The leaders of both teams are given a title and they have to draw it. The rest of the team has to guess. All the players have a turn at drawing a title. The team that guesses the most titles wins.

Telegrams

PREPARATIONS: Cut out words from newspaper headlines. (At least ten for each guest).

The players sit in a circle and are given five words each. They must start to make a sentence from the words they are given, but they may swap words with other players and with the pile of surplus words in the middle of the circle. The best sentence wins.

FOR THOSE WITH VERY PATIENT MOTHERS
Confetti Game

PREPARATIONS: Have ready two bowls full of confetti, two empty bowls and two dessert spoons.

Divide the guests into two teams. Line up the teams at one end of the room, with an empty bowl behind each team, and place the bowls of confetti at the opposite end of the room. The leaders of the teams are given a spoon each. They race to the full bowl, take a spoonful of confetti and carry it to the empty bowl. The second player in each team does the same. The team that finishes first wins IF it also has the most confetti in its bowl.

Scavenger

PREPARATIONS: None.

Tell the players to find objects whose first letters form a word, e.g. PUFFIN, Pin, Umbrella, Frock, Flannel, Ice, Nib. Tell the players the word they have to scavenge for before they begin. The first successful scavenger home wins and chooses the next word.

'... One unforgettable evening he said: "I've been writing a fantasy for young readers. ..." He read the first two chapters of **The Lion, the Witch and the Wardrobe.** Then stopped and said: "Do you think it's worth going on with?" '

by Roger Lancelyn Green

THERE is no bond like the bond of having read and liked the same books,' says somebody in one of E. Nesbit's stories: and that was how I got to know C. S. Lewis. I had been to his lectures and met him on more or less formal occasions, but this time we were at a wedding reception and both felt very out of it. We took our glasses of champagne into a window-recess, and were soon talking about George MacDonald and E. Nesbit and Rider Haggard. And then about stories of fantasy and imagination in general and why hardly anyone seemed to read them and publishers wouldn't publish them.

'Ah,' said Lewis, 'you wait until Tolkien's great book comes out . . . ! But I don't suppose he'll ever finish it!'

This was in 1945, and the book which Tolkien would never finish (because whenever he had time to get on with it, he spent most of it in revising what he had written) was *The Lord of the Rings.*

But the great change in readers' attitudes to stories of fantasy and imagination came before it was published – came with a book which Lewis himself produced in 1950: and I like to think that our conversation that day had a small share in bringing it into

being. For during our talk I had mentioned that I had just finished writing a fantasy, and with his usual generous interest in other people's work Lewis said: 'Do let me read it. Leave it for me at Magdalen as soon as you can.'

A week or two later he wrote me a long letter of criticism and advice about the book. But instead of returning it, he ended 'Come to dinner and collect the MS.' After this, dinners in Magdalen, with three or four hours talking books with Lewis in his rooms afterwards, became 'red-letter days' three or four times a year. Presently I rewrote my story, with some advice from him, and he said – and continued to say – that it was the best of its kind I had ever written (though it was never published).

Then one unforgettable evening he said: 'I've been writing a fantasy for young readers. May I read a bit of it to you?' He read the first two chapters of *The Lion, the Witch and the Wardrobe.* Then he stopped suddenly and said: 'Do you think it's worth going on with?'

I though it was well worth going on with, and told him so in no measured terms. For as he read there had crept over me a feeling of awe and excitement: not only that it was better than most children's books which were

appearing at the time – but the conviction that I was listening to the first reading of a great classic.

'I started it some time ago,' said Lewis, 'but it didn't work. There was no Aslan in it then. But just recently I saw how it ought to go, so I began again, and I can see it clearly right to the end. So I wrote these two chapters . . . But Tolkien doesn't like them . . . What do you really think?'

I told him again what I really thought, and pointed out how natural it was that Tolkien should not like it: for his fantasy world, the world of *The Hobbit*, was so very different – with a different greatness. As different, I think I said, as *The Princess and Curdie* from *The Wind in the Willows.*

Lewis saw my point – and he went on with the book. But I expect he would have gone on with it whatever I had said, for by now it was insisting on being written. It was not long, indeed, before one evening he handed me a big envelope and said: 'Here's the whole of that story I was writing. Take it away and give me your honest criticism.'

After that I carried away most of those precious manuscripts in their beautifully neat writing with hardly any corrections, and came back with criticism and praise, and still that

Illustrations by **Pauline Baynes**

growing wonder that is Narnia: a wonder that grows even now on each re-reading of the printed books. Sometimes Lewis agreed with my criticism: most of it was in *The Magician's Nephew* where a section of the book was scrapped and replaced, but I still wish he had omitted Father Christmas from *The Lion, the Witch and the Wardrobe* . . .

That, I think must have been a 'left-over' from the very first, pre-Aslan, idea for the book. It was a picture which was too vivid to be left out. For Lewis built up the Narnian stories from pictures, perhaps sometimes from dreams. He certainly dreamt vividly, and was subject to appalling nightmares: I remember once regretting that I remembered so few of my own dreams, even if they were nightmares: 'You may thank God that you don't,' he exclaimed with an intensity that made me start.

C. S. Lewis's childhood would seem unusual nowadays, and would indeed be almost impossible, however ordinary it was seventy years ago. 'In those days Mr. Sherlock Holmes was still living in Baker Street and the Bastables were looking for treasure in the Lewisham Road,' as he wrote of *The Magician's Nephew*: and if sometimes the children in the Narnian stories speak a little oddly, or seem to be imitating E. Nesbit's children, one

must remember that Lewis was himself a child when Nesbit was writing – and he is not borrowing from her, but both are giving us glimpses of 'the real thing.' While Nesbit had her own children and their friends to keep her up to date, Lewis remembered childhood mostly from his own experiences.

But they were pleasant years, spent mainly indoors, and most of the time in a rambling house on the outskirts of Belfast, in a perfect jungle of books. 'I am a product of long corridors, empty sunlit rooms, upstair indoor silences, attics explored in solitude, distant noises of gurgling cisterns and pipes, and the noise of wind under the tiles,' he wrote. 'Also, of endless books. My father bought all the books he read and never got rid of any of them. There were books in the study, books in the drawing-room, books (two deep) in the great bookcase on the landing, books

THE OLD GREY MARE
BY C. S. LEWIS (written at the the age of ten or eleven)

Round about the ladye's bower,
Round about the miller's tower,
Neath the shield
        and
O'er the field
Goes the old grey mare.

Rushing in some dreadful
   fray
SHE's a living shield I say,
Rushing o'er the bloody field,
She WILL face the foeman's
   shield.

Dash against some warhorse
   stronge
Midst a battle's bloody throng.
Though her rider dight in
   steels

The heavy thing she never
   feels.

When the bloody battle's over
Then is victory the rover.
For her feet there is the fen,
For her company the wren.
Far are known Knighthood,
But still more noble is the
   brood
Of the olde grey mare.

Round about the miller's tower,
Round about the ladye's bower,
Neath the shield
        and
O'er the field
Goes the old grey mare.

(C. S. Lewis's earliest surviving poem is published by permission of his Trustees and Literary Executors.)

in a bedroom, books piled as high as my shoulder in the cistern attic, books of all kinds . . . Nothing was forbidden me. In the seemingly endless rainy afternoons I took volume after volume from the shelves: I had always the same certainty of finding a book that was new to me as a man who walks into a field has of finding a new blade of grass.'

But, although the books included novels and works of humour, neither of his parents 'had the least taste for that kind of literature to which my allegiance was given the moment I could choose books for myself. Neither had ever listened to the horns of elfland. There was no copy of either Keats or Shelley in the house . . .'

Perhaps his first favourites among books intended for a young reader were the early Beatrix Potters which were just being published. Here he found real beauty in the pictures, and, with the aid of old volumes of *Punch*, the inspiration to begin writing stories about animals dressed and behaving like humans. These stories he continued for many years, producing whole histories of the imaginary land of Boxen, and joining them on to his brothers' less imaginative stories about India. But the Boxen stories were not like Narnia in any way except for being about an 'Animal Land.' There was no magic or fantasy: the stories

were indeed 'histories,' for all the time he was trying to write as much like a grown-up as possible, and about grown-up things, like politics, however little interested in them he really was.

However, overlapping and finally excluding this odd craze, came 'the horns of elfland' that were to lead him to his true kingdom. Old and young at the beginning of the century had a monthly treasure which has no parallel today: *The Strand Magazine*. Through this Lewis first found his way into the world of chivalry, led by Conan Doyle's *Sir Nigel*. But much better, he remembered, 'was E. Nesbit's trilogy, *Five Children and It, The Phoenix and the Carpet* and *The Amulet*.

It was when he was ten or eleven that romance began to creep into his writings. There was part of a story about vaguely medieval knights warring against each other and attacking castles, perhaps suggested by *Sir Nigel*; also his earliest surviving poem 'The Old Grey Mare' written before he was twelve shows in which direction his imagination was turning.

Not long after this Lewis suddenly became enslaved by the magic of Norse myth and legend – the wondrous tales of the gods of Asgard and the epics of the ancient Icelanders, with modern attempts to open windows into that world, such as Haggard's *Eric Brighteyes* and the great romances in

prose and verse by William Morris.

Out of all these worlds, and others too beyond number, grew the imagination which showed Lewis pictures that became his stories. At first vivid stories in verse, for to begin with he dreamt of being a great poet; but, when these did not prove successful, the poetic romances of other worlds; *Out of the Silent Planet* in 1938, the most memorable of all visits to Mars, and then *Perelandra,* with Lewis's most vivid and unforgettable pictures, of the great floating islands undulating upon the strange seas of the planet Venus.

And then after a pause pictures came suddenly again – vivid pictures, shaping themselves into a new form, suddenly, it seemed to Lewis, demanding that what he must write was that kind of literature which is called fantasy. For, as soon he realized: 'where the children's story is simply the right form for what the author has to say, then of course readers who want to hear that, will read the story or re-read it at any age . . .

Looking back over the twenty years since readers entered Narnia for the first time, I feel sure that we can claim those seven marvellous tales as among the 'good ones' that last. Indeed, I think they have already won their place among the very few great books of their special kind which will go on lasting.

What C. S. Lewis has said about his work :—

'In a certain sense I have never actually "made" a story. With me the process is much more like bird-watching than either talking or building. I see pictures. Sometimes these pictures have a common flavour, almost a common smell, which groups them together. Keep quiet and watch and they will begin joining themselves up. If you were very lucky (I have never been as lucky as all that) a whole set might join themselves so consistently that there you had a complete story: without doing anything yourself. But more often (in my experience always) there are gaps. Then at last you have to do some deliberate inventing, have to contrive reasons why these characters should be in these various places doing these various things. I have no idea whether this is the usual way of writing stories, still less whether it is the best. It is the only one I know: images always come first.'

And about *The Lion, the Witch and the Wardrobe* he wrote: 'all began with a picture of a Faun carrying an umbrella and parcels in a snowy wood. This picture had been in my mind since I was about sixteen. Then one day, when I was about forty, I said to myself: "Let's try to make a story about it". At first I had very little idea how the story would go. But then suddenly Aslan came bounding into it. I think I had been having a good many dreams about lions about that time. Apart from that, I don't know where the Lion came from or why He came. But once He was there He pulled the whole story together, and soon He pulled the six other Narnian stories after him.'

Michael Bond introduces Olga da Polga

"the guinea pig of the year"

IF you think about it, many of the important things in one's life happen quite by chance, simply because you happen to be in a certain place at a certain time. At least, it's always been that way with me. That's how it was with Paddington and the same thing happened again with Olga.

I wanted to buy my daughter a guinea-pig for her birthday and because it was a nice, sunny day we decided to drive the twenty or so miles to Basingstoke where I remembered once seeing a pet shop. I suppose we *could* have found a dozen other shops nearer at hand, but if we had we would never have met Olga.

Once we got her home the inevitable happened. In no time at all, like Paddington before her, she wormed her way into our affections to such an extent that I simply had to write about her.

The first few stories were very short and were written for a local magazine, as much for my own amusement as for any other reason.

It wasn't until last year, when I happened to tell Kaye about them and she suggested I might have a book on my hands – another act of chance – that work began in earnest; rewriting, revising, dreaming up new stories to fit the title, and enjoying many happy sessions with **Hans Helweg,** who has brought his own special magic to work in the drawings.

In a way Olga and Paddington are somewhat alike. Life is never dull when they're around – and if it is they soon

change all THAT. But there the resemblance ends, for whereas Paddington is a bear with his two back paws planted firmly on the ground in all senses of the word, Olga lives her life with her head very much in the clouds, enjoying wild and fanciful thoughts of a kind that would never enter Paddington's head for a moment, although I'm sure he would be most impressed by some of them.

There *are* humans in the book, but Olga's world is mostly concerned with other animals who live in the neighbourhood; **Fangio,** a hedgehog with a taste for adventure, who lives in a garage down the road and is believed to have Argentinian blood; **Noel,** the cat, who is secretly rather overawed by his new companion; **Graham,** the tortoise . . . they all have a part to play.

Animals, however small, have a way of making their feelings known, and Olga is no exception. Over the years she has laid down the law on a variety of subjects, from her dislike of grass picked from the side of main roads (however green it looks it always tastes of diesel fumes!), to being cleaned out when all SHE wants is a quiet afternoon nap.

Many of the stories actually took place. Others are what I like to call 'tales that might have been.' The rest, I'm afraid, are the product of Olga's own fertile imagination (with a little help from me!).

EDITOR'S NOTE: This article appeared in Puffin Post Vol. 5 No. 3 (1971) and Olga turned out to be so popular that Michael Bond was persuaded to write another book about her, in which she meets another guinea-pig called Boris.

At first she didn't understand why it was that one night he behaved like a Russian Prince, the next like a cowboy and the third like a gangster, but then she discovered he was a T.V. watcher. So the second book is called OLGA MEETS HER MATCH.

Tale The Fourth

THE CLOCK
by Russell Hoban

Illustrated by Fritz Wegner

THE clock, ticking and tocking, swinging his pendulum behind the glass front of his case and striking the hours day and night, thought long about the things that had happened in the room. He had seen the tin frog find a way into the picture with La Corona; he had seen the tin horseman break the enchantment of the yellow-haired princess; he had heard the night watchman cry out in words that made the tin crocodile compose poetry. The clock noticed that the crucial moment was always just after his hands touched midnight and just before he sounded his twelve strokes.

He thought about it more and more, and he began to feel left out because he himself could never do anything in that inbetween moment except go on keeping time. 'Of course,' he said to himself, 'keeping time is very important. I am sure it is more important than anything those others have done.'

He went on ticking and tocking and striking the hours. 'All the same,' he said to himself, 'sometimes I wonder whether I keep time or time keeps me. In a way I am really no better than a prisoner on a treadmill, walking day and night my tick-tock wheel.'

The clock was wound once a week. As the time for each new winding approached he could feel his mainspring losing power. He determined to stop his pendulum, if he could, just at that moment when his hands touched midnight and before he struck the twelve strokes.

On the night before the morning when he was to be wound again he felt the looseness of his mainspring, felt how little force there was in the swinging pendulum and in the tick-tock wheel that kept him walking. Ten o'clock came, half-past ten, eleven o'clock, half-past eleven. His hands touched twelve and, gathering all his strength, the clock exerted his will upon the pendulum. The pendulum stopped. The clock had not struck. The two little brass legs of his escapement stopped walking. 'Anything can happen,' said the clock.

Leaving the rest of his works behind, he slipped out of his case, just the two little walking brass legs of him, and walked down the wall.

In the picture inside the cigar-box lid La Corona and the tin frog listened for the twelve strokes of midnight, but heard nothing. The coloured dots of the picture moved apart, moved farther and farther apart. 'Hold me tight,' said La Corona to the tin frog. 'I am only coloured dots like the rest of the picture.'

'No,' said the tin frog. 'You are no longer only a picture, you are my beloved.' He held her tight, and she stayed together as they dropped out of the lid into the cigar-box, and the magnifying glass, the seashell, and the tape measure fell with them.

They climbed out of the cigar-box, down from the shelf, and stood in the moonlight on the oriental carpet. On the wall the dim hands of the clock stood motionless at midnight.

On the rocky island on the card by the window the weather castle vanished, and the tin horseman and his princess galloped over the blue sea as it disappeared, then leaped down to the carpet with the others.

The incense-burning night watchman found that he could speak the language of the others. 'Now is the only time there is!' was the first thing he said.

The tin crocodile, who had been

thinking over his poems, said, 'I haven't even *begun* to make poetry yet.'

The spinster mouse editor shot out of the hole in the skirting board and said, 'Quarterly is not enough!'

'Who's keeping time now?' said the magnifying glass.

'Time can't be kept,' said the brass legs of the clock's escapement. 'And time can't keep you.' Across the oriental carpet he marched in the moonlight, up the wall, and stood on the sill of the open window. As he marched he sang, 'Ting-tang, tantarang!'

Everyone followed him across the carpet and up to the windowsill.

'Where will our next castle be, I wonder?' said the yellow-haired princess to the tin horseman.

'What do you suppose the new picture will be?' said La Corona to the tin frog.

'Now!' said the incense-burning night watchman.

'Deep!' said the seashell.

'Thousands and thousands of leagues by the inch!' said the tape measure.

'Pay close attention!' said the magnifying glass.

'Every day!' said the spinster mouse editor.

'Ting-tang, tantarang!' sang the marching brass legs of the clock's escapement, and they all followed him out through the window and into the moonlight. Last of all was whoever lived in the round yellow glass-topped box that had been the monkey game of skill.

'They'll want me too,' he said. 'Everyone can't be nice.'

JOKES by Puffineers

Boy: I think our teacher's crazy, he talks to himself.
Girl: So does ours, but he thinks we're listening!

1st Tree: How did you sleep last night?
2nd Tree: Like a log.
Two oranges rolling down a hill. One stopped. Why?
Because it ran out of juice.

What shakes at the bottom of the sea?
A nervous wreck!
What one strawberry said to the other: 'If you hadn't been so fresh we wouldn't be in this jam'.

The Ship in the Bottle

by
BARBARA SLEIGH

The Ship in the Bottle was in old Barty Digweed's house next door. It stood on the mantelshelf among the pipes, unemptied ash-trays, and strange odds and ends that the old man had collected in his long life at sea.

On Saturday mornings Johnny would go and see if he could run any errands for Mr Digweed, who had a wooden leg. Johnny was the only person he would allow inside the house.

'I don't want no women cluttering up the place!' the old man said. 'Once they start tidying me up I shan't ever find nothing again.' And he would puff at his evil-smelling pipe, and look round with contentment at the wild disorder of the room. 'Just hand me my baccy tin,' he might go on. 'It's under the dirty dishes on the draining board. Now, did I ever tell you about that time I was on board the Griffin? —Ship's Cook I was – ah, those were the days!—and the Captain's spectacles got swallowed by a walrus?'

And old Barty would yarn away about man-eating sharks, and flying fishes, and icebergs as big as Windsor Castle; about shipwrecks, and forty-foot waves, and mutineers. Sometimes Johnny wondered if quite so many adventures could possibly have happened to one man, even with such a long life as old Barty's. But, even better than the story-telling, sometimes he would take the Ship in the Bottle down from its shelf, and let Johnny hold it.

It was an ordinary glass bottle, with its cork glued firmly into place. Johnny could feel with his fingers the words 'Jobson's Jamaica Rum' in raised glass letters on the back, but inside its shining curved sides was a magic world. A three-masted ship, in full sail, forever rode upon an emerald sea, the water frothing white at her bows with the speed of her going. Perfect she was in every detail, shrouds, halyards, all her tackle complete: and her name, *Esperance* (which old Barty made rhyme with Nancy) in ant-sized letters on her side. The tallest mast was no higher than the first two joints of Johnny's little finger.

'Did you really make it, Mr Digweed?' asked Johnny the first time he saw it. The old man nodded.

'Masts, mizzen, spanker and jib. Made the lot of 'em! My mascot that is. Goes with me on every voyage.'

'But how did you get the ship inside the bottle?' asked Johnny, and Old Barty made the hoarse noise that passed with him as a chuckle.

'Ah, that'd be telling.' And not a word more would he say.

Johnny stared at the ship, and the little quay behind with its cluster of houses, and the lighthouse on the tiny promontory. He stared at it so hard that he could see the whole scene exactly as it was, even when he closed his eyes.

And then one day Mr Digweed said he was going away. 'Can't afford to stay,' he said. 'They've put up the rent. I've got to go and live with my Married Daughter, worse luck.'

'Won't you like that?'

'I shall hate it!' said the old man frankly. 'She don't like me smoking me pipe for one thing.'

'But shan't I ever see you or the Ship in the Bottle again?' asked Johnny sadly.

'I don't suppose so,' said the old man, with a sorrowful shake of the head. 'I shouldn't mind going so much if there'd be youngsters about, but she don't like children, my Married Daughter don't.'

'Couldn't you go to sea again, instead?' asked Johnny.

'Not a hope. No one would want an ancient old cock like me, with a pegleg what's more. But I tell you what, Johnny boy; the night before I go I'll let you take the old *Esperance* home! You can bring it back in the morning.'

And so it was that one day Johnny took the Ship in the Bottle home. He sat and gloated over it till bed-time, and, so that he shouldn't miss a minute of looking at it, when he had his bath he lodged it between the piece of soap and the nail brush on the sponge rack.

He didn't mean to drop it in the hot water. It just fell in with a splash, when he pulled his face-flannel out from underneath. Luckily it floated. For a moment Johnny was horrified, then he said to himself:

'I don't suppose it will hurt really. It's got a cork, so the water can't get inside, and it probably likes floating on a different, bigger sea.'

He made waves with his hands, and sailed it round the twin pink islands of his knees, and watched it rise and fall on the swell of a mighty storm

he made by paddling his feet.

'Johnny!' called his mother at last from downstairs. 'It's high time you were out of that bath and in bed!'

'Just coming!' he called back, and then he said softly, 'Look out, the tide's going down!' And he pulled the plug out with his toes and jumped out onto the bath-mat. And as he dried himself he watched the Ship in the Bottle twist round and round in the whirlpool over the plug hole, and come to a clattering stop as the water drained away.

When he got into bed he propped his treasure up beside him so that he could still see it, even when his head was on the pillow. Suddenly he sat up again. Something about it was different? The sails were no longer bellying out as though being carried along by a stiff breeze. They were

neatly furled. The anchor was down and the sea was lapping gently against her sides. He could actually see her rising and falling on the gentle swell. It was growing dusk in the tiny world of the bottle, and the bright eye of the little lighthouse winked in a friendly way.

'Dang me dead-eyes!' breathed Johnny (an expression he had picked up from old Barty). Gingerly he tried the cork. The glue, which usually held it firmly in place, had been softened by the hot bath water, and

111

it came out quite easily. He screwed up one eye and peered inside. The opening was so small he could see little, but he could hear the murmur of the sea quite distinctly, and was it? ... could it be ...? the cry of a sea-gull? and the far distant sound of singing? But so small, *so* small was the sound that the singers might have been no bigger than green-fly! Very gingerly Johnny poked a finger into the bottle to feel if the sea really was wet. When he drew it out again there was a drop of moisture on the end. Sea-water? Rum? After all, it was a rum bottle. There was only one way of finding out. Johnny put his finger in his mouth. It tasted salt. And then it happened.

He suddenly felt dizzy, so he closed his eyes. When he opened them again he was not in his bedroom any longer. He was standing in the opening of what seemed like a circular tunnel, the sides of which felt cold and smooth. There was a steep slope at his feet. He took a step forward, stumbled and slid down its slippery surface. Luckily he landed on soft grass at the bottom. He picked himself up and made for a rough track he could just see in the twilight. Not far away on the right was a group of houses. On the left was the sea—and, rising and falling gently on the water, was a great three-masted ship.

As soon as Johnny saw the ship he began to run towards it. Presently the path became paved, and led shortly to a small quay, and there, towering above him, her sails furled and the anchor down was the *Esperance*!

'It is!' said Johnny. 'It really is! I'm inside the ship in the bottle! It must have happened somehow when I licked my finger.'

A sea-gull gave a mocking cry, and there was a burst of laughter and singing from one of the houses on his right. It was larger than the other buildings and there was a swinging

inn sign over the door. The Weather-Eye and Winkle it said. Johnny stole up to the open door and peered into a lamplit room.

A number of rough-looking men were sitting at a table, smoking and drinking. They shouted with laughter at some joke, and then one man, sitting at a separate table near the blazing log fire, suddenly roared:

'Belay there, you rascals! I said you could drink my health now you've signed on for the voyage, but we sail on the first tide tomorrow. I shall expect you all aboard the *Esperance* by daylight. And sober, mind!'

The noise quietened down, and there were mutterings of 'Ay, Ay, Cap'en!'

'Now, Mister Mate,' said the man they addressed as Captain. 'The crew's complete except for ship's cook and cabin boy ...' He broke off suddenly. 'Well shiver me shrouds! What's that peering through the door there? The very article! come here, boy!'

Johnny looked round, and seeing he was the only boy in sight, stepped shyly up to the table.

'What's your name, hey?' said the Captain gruffly.

'Johnny, sir.'

'Ever been to sea, Johnny?'

'No, sir.'

'Hm,' said the Captain. 'Well, you look an upstanding lad. Like to ship as cabin boy?'

''You mean on the *Esperance*? Ooh, yes!' said Johnny eagerly. ''I mean, ay, ay, sir,' he added.

'Sixpence a week and double grog on Sundays. That shows what an open-handed man I am. Sign him on, Mister Mate; and if you can't write, boy, make your cross!'

Johnny picked up the quill pen rather slowly. He didn't feel that sixpence a week was very much, and he wasn't sure if he would like grog. He was just going to sign when he heard the Captain say: 'Time's getting short, Mister Mate. I'd sign on a ship's cook if he was as old as Methus-

elah, with a peg-leg into the bargain!'

Johnny put the pen down again without signing. He didn't know how old Methuselah was, or Mr Digweed, but it didn't seem to matter.

'Please, sir!' he said. 'I believe I could find you a ship's cook!'

'You could?' said the Captain. 'Then what are you waiting for? Crowd on all canvas, and overhaul him, boy!'

Johnny turned and ran as fast as he could, out of the Weather-Eye and Winkle, along the quay and the paved road. By the time he reached the rough path he was quite out of breath. It was then that a horrid thought struck him. Just suppose that his mother, in one of her tidying-up fits, had picked up the cork and put it back in the bottle! He pulled up short. 'I wouldn't be able to get out and tell old Barty that he could go to sea again after all,' he said. 'I might not ever get out of the bottle again!'

It was one thing to go for a voyage as cabin boy and come back triumphant, and boast about your adventures,

but quite another to stay inside the bottle until someone chanced to take the cork out again! Johnny began to run, more desperately now.

'Thank goodness . . . I never signed on! I must . . . get out . . . in time . . .!' he panted.

On he went, stumbling along the rough track, with only one thought in his mind. His heart was thumping painfully as he took the slippery slope that led to the mouth of the tunnel. Twice he fell back, but at last he managed to scramble up on his hands and knees. If the opening at the end was dark it would mean the cork was in the bottle! He looked down the round tunnel. Thank Heavens he could see light! He hurried to the opening, and just as he got there the same dizzy feeling came over him as before, and he closed his eyes.

When he opened them again he was sitting up in bed, and the Ship in the Bottle was on the table exactly where he had left it, its sails still furled, but his mother, with her back towards him, was just stooping to pick something up off the floor. She gave a start when she stood up and saw Johnny.

'Oh, you did make me jump! I never heard you come in and get into bed! But how naughty of you to take the cork out of Mr Digweed's beautiful bottle! I was just going to put it back again!'

As she spoke she pushed it firmly home.

'There,' she said. 'That won't come out again in a hurry.'

'Phew!' said Johnny to himself. 'Thank goodness! I don't suppose I'd be allowed to go round to old Barty now. I shall just have to wait till Mum and Dad are having supper.' He lay back on the pillow and closed his eyes . . . and somehow when he opened them again it was morning. Johnny leapt out of bed.

'If old Barty's going to sign on, I must hurry. She sails on the morning tide!' he said.

He found the old man already sitting in his armchair, looking sadly round his old home. Johnny rushed in and pushed the Ship in the Bottle into his hands and burst out excitedly: 'Mr Digweed! Mr Digweed! You needn't look sad! You haven't got to go and live with your Married Daughter. You can sign on as ship's cook on the *Esperance*! And it doesn't matter about your peg-leg, and being as old as Methuselah!' And out poured the whole story of his adventure. 'You just stick your finger in the bottle, and lick the wetness that comes out on the end of it ... and ... well, it happens.'

Old Barty smiled wanly.

'It's good of you to come and cheer me up with your tales, Johnny boy, but there's no help for it. I shall have to go. I know all about making up stories, none better!' He gave one of his rusty chuckles. 'We've been good friends, you and me. But you'd best be off or you'll be late for school. Give us your paw!'

Sadly Johnny held out a limp hand. It was all no good he thought. The old man didn't believe him. They shook hands.

'So long matey!' said old Barty.

'So long,' said Johnny soberly, and turned to go.

When he got to the door he turned and said sadly:

'I *didn't* make it up. And you haven't once looked at the *Esperance* and seen how her sails are furled, and how real wet waves are lapping all round her!'

For the first time old Barty did look at the Ship in the Bottle, which he was still holding. He stared at it intently, with a gathering frown.

'She sails on the first tide,' said

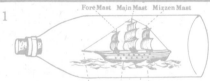

How to make a ship in a bottle

Now you've ready my story I think you deserve to be told how Mr Digweed got his ship in the bottle, and you might like to try to do it. I won't pretend that it isn't difficult, but that makes it all the more exciting if you manage to pull it off ... or UP: for that is the secret.

He made the *Esperance* outside the bottle, sails, rigging, masts, all complete, but he put a tiny wire hinge at the base of each mast, so that all three could lie flat while the ship was pushed through the neck of the bottle.

When it was in place, he pulled them up again by means of a thread tied to the top of the foremast, fixed the thread to the bowsprit and: 'Dang me dead-eyes!' as he might have said, 'Stow your cork home, and ... there you are!' This is how you set about it.

Sharp knife for carving hull; Medium size needle and thimble; Old table knife; Two fine cheap paint brushes; Piece of strong wire two feet long; Suitable bottle with a short neck; Wood for the hull, about $2\frac{1}{2}" \times \frac{3}{4}"$, and a flat piece to make a stand for the bottle; Two slats to be glued along the long edges of the stand to stop the bottle from rolling off; Putty; Cocktail sticks for masts, yards and bowsprit (see diagram); Thread for rigging; Durofix glue; Fine wire for hinges; Tiny tins of enamel paint.

Curl up both ends

1 Carve the hull, making it as much like diagram 3 as possible.

2. With the bottle on its side, take little lumps of putty between the tweezers and poke them through the bottle neck until you have enough putty inside, and squash it flat with the end of the table knife. (Diagram 4.) Then ruffle the surface with the end of the knife to look like waves.

3. While the putty is setting paint the hull of your ship. When the paint is dry measure your masts; the main mast is the tallest, the mizzen the shortest. Mark carefully on the deck where each one is to stand. Do not make mizzen mast longer than $2\frac{1}{4}"$. Remember it has to be able to clear the top of the bottle when pulled upright.

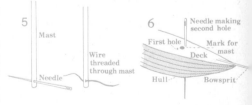

HULL   Plan of deck

Plan of masts and wire holes

Side view

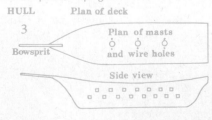

4. Make a hole, using the needle, through the bottom of each mast (diagram 5) and thread a 3" piece of wire through.

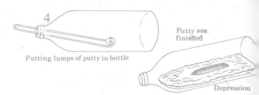

5. Now, with the needle, make a hole clean through to the bottom of the hull on *either side* of the place you have marked on the deck for the masts (diagram 6).

6. Next make the bowsprit. Cut about $\frac{1}{2}"$ of cocktail stick and glue it into place. Remember that this has to take

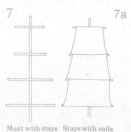

Mast with stays   Stays with sails

Johnny. But old Barty didn't seem to hear. He was still staring with astonishment at the Ship in the Bottle.

Johnny closed the door behind him and went home.

Late that afternoon Mr Digweed's Married Daughter knocked on the door. Both her heels and her voice were very high and sharp.

'Have you seen anything of my old dad?' she asked. 'I can't understand it. He knew I was coming for him first thing, and there's not a sign of him anywhere. I've been waiting all this time. He hasn't taken his money, or his overcoat, or his best leg. It's still in the wardrobe—and his suitcase all ready packed. And another thing: that old Ship in a Bottle he set such store by—Well, the bottle's there, but the little ship's gone! She held out the bottle to show them its emptiness.

Johnny took it in both hands. 'Where-ever can my old dad have gone?'

'Sailed on the morning tide!' whispered Johnny.

'What's that?' asked Mr Digweed's Married Daughter sharply.

'Oh, nothing,' said Johnny, and under pretence of peering into the empty bottle he whispered: 'So long—matey!'

Nobody ever saw old Barty again. When at last the house next door was sold up and emptied, Johnny found the Bottle sticking out of the dustbin. He has it still: but just in case one day the *Esperance* should come sailing back to the little quay, and old Barty want to come home and tell him his adventures, no one is ever allowed to put the cork back in again.

drawings by SCOULAR ANDERSON

---

the strain of the thread which finally holds up the masts, so see it is secure.

7. Glue the stays (the cross pieces of wood that carry the sails) to the masts. (Diagram 7.) Make them narrow enough to pass through the neck of the bottle. Cut sails from white paper and glue them to the stays (7a).

8. Now, you remember the wire you threaded through the base of each mast? Very carefully thread the two ends of each through the holes you have already made right through the hull, and twist them together at the bottom of the ship. These are the hinges. Do not twist them so tightly that you can't move the masts up and down. Trim off unwanted wire. (Diagrams 8 and 9.)

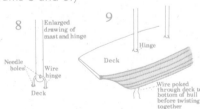

9. Glue the end of a 12" piece of thread to the centre of the stern; then with the mizzen mast (1) standing upright, tie the thread to the top, then take it across to the main mast (2) and tie, and last to the foremast (3) leaving a long loose end. (Diagram 10.) You should now be able to lower all three masts so that they are almost flat on

the deck, by pulling on the long thread. Very gently practise raising and lowering the masts. (Diagram 10a.)

10. Put a tiny dab of glue at the top of each mast to stop thread from slipping.

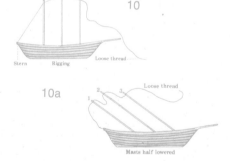

11. Take a second 12" thread, make a small loop at one end and fix it over the top of the fore mast, so that you have two loose ends.

12. Now comes the great moment! *If* the putty is set, and the paint and glue dry, and the masts can be raised very carefully from their lowered position, you are ready to ease the ship into the bottle . . . With the masts down, grip the hull firmly with the tweezers and *coat the flat bottom of the hull with glue*. Then *very carefully* slide the ship into the bottle and press it gently into the putty depression you have already made for it. Remove tweezers. You now should have the two strands of thread hanging out of the bottle (diagram 11).

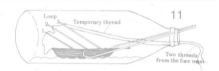

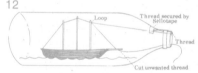

13. Now comes the hardest bit of all. You *must wait* until the glue holding the ship in position is *quite* dry! If you try to pull the masts up before it has set the whole thing will probably be wrecked. I recommend putting the ship out of reach of anyone who might be tempted to give the threads an ill-timed tweak, and leave it until next day. THEN, very, very carefully pull the thread that is looped over the top of the fore mast until all three masts are standing squarely upright, and fix the thread securely to the *outside* of the bottle with a piece of sellotape (diagram 12). This is only a temporary support while you glue the thread that is the rigging to the end of the bowsprit. When this final gluing is *quite* firm and dry, carefully un-peel the sellotape and lever off the loop from the top of the fore mast. Snip off the unwanted thread from the bowsprit, put in the cork—and there's your Ship in a Bottle. No promises that you can go exploring like Johnny, but it *will* be a great achievement.

Diagrams by Conrad Bailey

My Mother's Frilly Parasol

CYNTHIA HARNET

This story is really a little bit of history though I certainly did not think so at the time. It happened to me when I was quite a small girl. Queen Victoria was still on the throne and any story which goes back as far as that must be a part of history anyway.

It was in London on a Sunday, a bright summer day, and I was walking beside my mother on our way back from church. I wore a clean starched frock that scratched and silk gloves which I hated because they creaked and set my teeth on edge. My mother's dress had lots of frills and flounces almost to the ground. She wore a hat with feathers and she carried a frilly parasol.

We were walking along the pavement beside the big main road which runs from Kensington to Hammersmith; those of you who live in London may know it. It has not changed very much except for the roar of the modern traffic which thunders all day long. But at the time that I am talking of the noise was only the clip clop of horses' hoofs and the grinding of wooden wheels on the dusty road. There were fine open carriages with coachmen on the box, light dog carts, pony carts and even donkey carts spinning along, besides rumbling old horse buses and swift hansom cabs on two high wheels, with their drivers perched up at the back. There was always plenty to look at though there were practically no motor cars. I had only seen one or two in my whole life; they were something one could go home and brag about.

At one side of the road the pavement ran along by a high brick wall with a line of terrace houses built behind it. The wall seemed to go on for ever and for somebody who could not see over the top it was very dull, with nothing to watch but the traffic. On this Sunday morning

Manners of Girls

there happened to be a red horse bus drawn up at the road-side while somebody climbed up to a seat on the roof. The bus completely blocked my view, so I turned round to see if there was anything more interesting coming along at the back. Then I pulled my mother's hand to make her look round too.

Beside the far end of the pavement stood a tall dog cart with bright yellow wheels. It was evidently something special because the young man on the box was very smart; he sat very upright holding the reins firmly with both hands, waiting for the bus to move on. The horse, a tall chestnut with an arched neck, was prancing between the shafts as though eager to be off.

Suddenly from across the road came the loud POOP POOP of a motor horn. Instantly the horse reared right up and then began to plunge and kick wildly out behind. There was the sound of splintering wood as the dog cart was smashed to pieces, and, before we had time to take it in, the chestnut horse, driver-less but with the yellow wheels still attached, was charging towards us.

We were in direct line between the wall and the bus. I can remember that, screaming with terror, I struggled to run away, but my mother had me firmly by the hand and she ran not away but towards that terrible horse, waving her frilly parasol.

To me it seemed she was mad, but the horse, faced with this female of the human species in defence of her young, preferred the bus. There was a dreadful screaming and clattering and crashing of glass, but I was too lost in bellowing to take it in. But my mother still had a firm grip on me, and regardless of my sobs she turned me right round and led me off briskly towards home.

'Come along, child,' she said, 'hurry, or we'll be late.'

Not until later, when my father had been told, and she had been pressed into an armchair and given a glass of wine, did I begin to realize that my mother had done something wonderful.

Later still, when I asked what had happened next, I was told that nobody had been badly hurt, and I hoped that it included the horse. But it was a very long time before I could be induced to walk along that piece of pavement again.

Actually the pavement is still there, with the wall and the line of houses behind it. It is called Earl's Terrace. I passed it last month, and I think, even now, that I was glad that I was in a car.

PUZZLERS

set by **MICHAEL HOLT**

organized and embellished by **GRAHAM ROUND**

SAFARI ARK

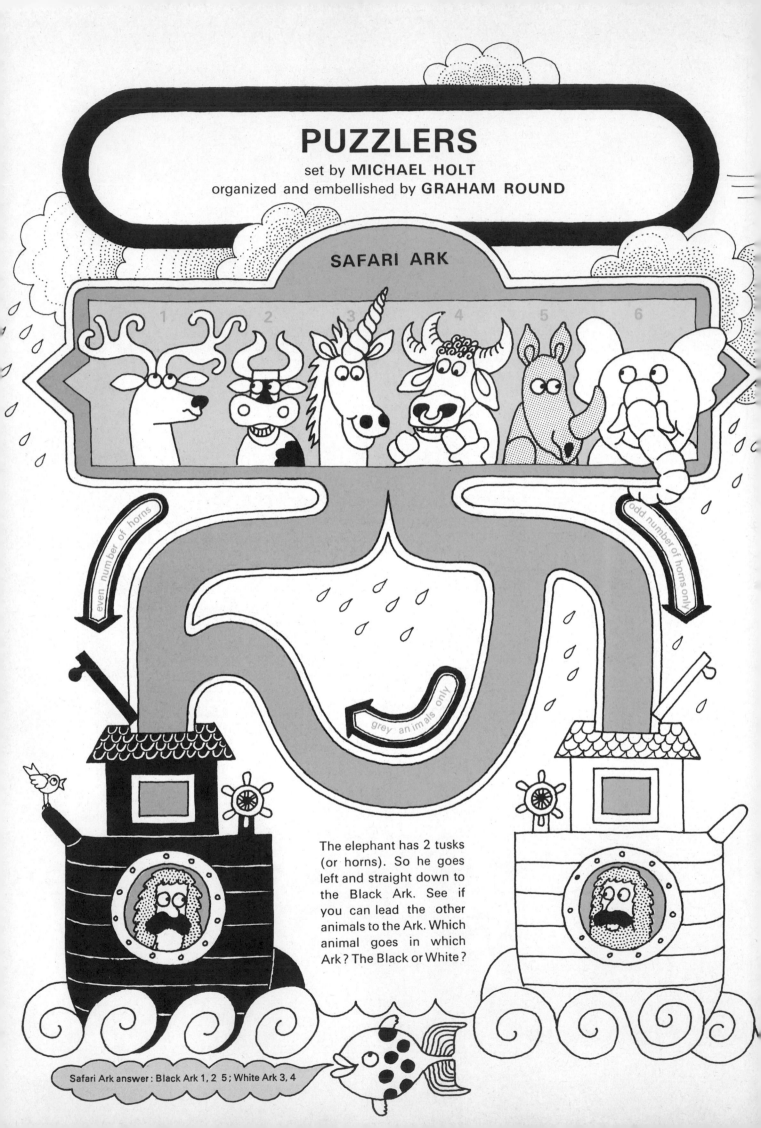

even number of horns

odd number of horns only

grey animals only

The elephant has 2 tusks (or horns). So he goes left and straight down to the Black Ark. See if you can lead the other animals to the Ark. Which animal goes in which Ark? The Black or White?

Safari Ark answer: Black Ark 1, 2 5; White Ark 3, 4

Simple Simon · **How many lemonades has Simon still got?**

NEXT MOMENT

NEXT BEAD

Which bead goes next?

Can you spot the pattern?

Pick from the box

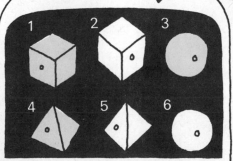

1 2 3
4 5 6

STICKY PROBLEM

How can you make 4 equal triangles out of these 9 matchsticks?

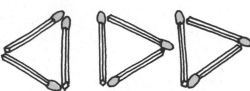

Easy? Now make 4 triangles out of 6 matchsticks.

Number Forcing Trick

Say to a friend: 'Think of a number – any number – and spell it out in full in words. Count the number of letters and spell that number out in letters. Go on again and again.' Now you can bet your friend that he will end up with FOUR. It is a dead end, for it changes into itself because it has 4 letters.

For example:

Fifty-three → Ten
(10 letters) (3 letters)
→ Three → Five
(5 letters) (4 letters)
→ Four
(4 letters)

See if you can find a number that doesn't go to FOUR. If you do, please write to me about it. I bet you don't – find a number, I mean.

Counting sheep problem

A young friend of mine Marcus Boll (10) put this poser to me. See if you can do it. A farmer had a vast flock of sheep and he found that when he divided the number of sheep in it by 2 he had one over; but he also found he had one over when he divided by 3, by 4, by 5 . . . all the way up to 10. What was the smallest size of flock he could have had?

(Too hard? Then work out the smallest flock that leaves one over when divided just by 2, by 3 and by 4. It's not $2 \times 3 \times 4 + 1$ (or 25): that's not the *smallest* flock possible. Remember, 2 goes into 4. So if the flock is divisible by 4 with one over, so it must be when divided by 2.)

Counting Sheep
Ans: 2521. The answer is *not* got by multiplying all the numbers from 2 to 10 inclusive, $2 \times 3 \times 4 . . . \times 9 \times 10 = 3,628,800$, and adding 1 to it. For we said the *smallest flock* possible.

Simple Simon
Ans: 3 glasses

Next Bead

Sticky Problem

Make SMILERS and SCOWLERS with Michael Grater

SMILERS can be made from any piece of paper or card. If we start with a simple shape, add two eyes, a nose and a smiling mouth we can surround ourselves with SMILERS.

If we can make SMILERS as easily as this we can try varying them in different ways –

What else can we do with our SMILERS? We can give them bright and cheerful things to wear. We might make SMILERS with Ties. These can be cut from patterned wrapping paper. They can be fixed easily if an extra flap is included at the top for sticking.

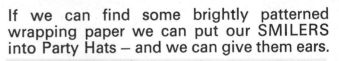

We can make SMILERS with hair. We can cut paper into different patterns at the edges and can add it to the faces. There are many different edge patterns we can find. The added hair shapes can also be patterned.

If we can find some brightly patterned wrapping paper we can put our SMILERS into Party Hats – and we can give them ears.

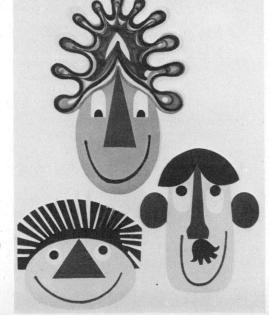

120

We could have SMILERS on the wall with rosettes in team colours – our own special team supporters.

There are many other different SMILERS for us to make. If we put ears on our SMILERS we might add ear-rings – again large and brightly patterned.

This time when we use our SMILERS as decorations we might fold them vertically through the centre so that they stand out slightly from the wall. The fold will make the paper SMILERS slightly stronger.

If we find that the fold makes our SMILERS stronger we might try standing them up – making perhaps Man and Wife SMILERS. These can be made to stand with only a single fold through the centre. We can use specially selected patterns from wrapping paper for the clothes. Or we can decorate them ourselves.

Standing SMILERS can be made in many different shapes – Clowns perhaps, or any other happy people we can think of.

There are other ways of making our SMILERS stand. They can be set into slots cut into the top of a toilet-roll core. This can also be covered with patterned paper.

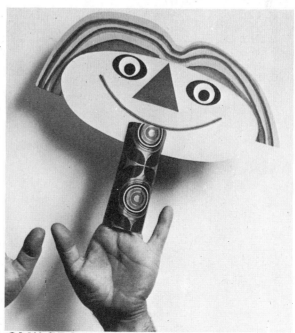

SMILERS made like this can be used as Hand Puppets.

121

Box SMILERS might also be used as containers for other things. We might use them as table decorations for a party – they could hold the paper napkins.

If we can find suitable cardboard containers we can make SMILERS as Money Boxes. We can seal the box with sticky tape and can cut a slot into the top for the coins. The SMILER'S face can either be drawn on the box or cut separately and fixed to it.

Like SMILERS – SCOWLERS can be made with many different characteristics. We could make a family of SCOWLERS and could hang them together as a mobile, but these would need pattern on both sides because they would move when hung up.

But we might not always be in a party mood. Look at the Reflecting SMILERS – and then turn the page upside down. SMILERS like any of us can also be SCOWLERS.

SMILERS are fun to make for a party. But if you are not lucky enough to be having a party – you could make some SMILERS anyway. They will cheer you up – or your friends. And you will enjoy making them – or some SCOWLERS if that is how you feel.

But make them with lots of pattern and lots of colour.

Save and use your wrapping paper. SMILERS can be small – or large. You can pin them to the wall, stick them to the window, hang them up or stand them.

And if you are not too keen on human SMILERS or SCOWLERS – you might make them as animals. You could fold them and send them to your friends as greetings cards. SMILERS or SCOWLERS – all you need are some odd scraps of paper or cardboard – some scissors – and some glue.

SMILERS – even SCOWLERS – are fun to make.

SPORTS QUIZ

Every picture has a question – how many can you answer?

1. Who is he? Where was it? Did he win? **2.** How many men? What are they doing? **3.** Male or female? What sport? **4.** What teams? Where? Who won? **5.** How many men in the boat? **6.** How did he get this high? Can you recognise who it is? **7.** Perfect stance, but for what sport? **8 & 9.** Two more tireless athletes, what are they doing?

2

4

3

6

8

7

9

ANSWERS: 1. Ilie Nastase, winning at Wimbledon 1972 *(picture by Chris Smith)*. 2. Two men wrestling. 3. Peter Shilton (goalkeeper for Leicester City). 4. International Rugby at Twickenham 1974, Ireland beating England. 5. The usual number for a Boat Race team (this one is Cambridge in 1973)—just Chris Smith's special magic. 6. Brian Hooper's winning vault in the Commonwealth Games 1973 *(picture by Mervyn Rees)*. 7. Cricket—it's Trevor Bailey. 8. & 9. High jumping (C. Pardee). Tennis (Roger Taylor). *Outine pictures supplied by Sport and General.*

Answer to question on p. 29: The camera was on the masthead. Chris Smith, the photographer, was behind the sails at remote control of a motor driven Nikon. The catamaran was *The Lady B* taking part in the world speed championships in Portland Harbour 1973.

5